THE DISCOVERY
── OF THE ──
LAKE DISTRICT

A NORTHERN ARCADIA AND ITS USES

VICTORIA
& ALBERT
MUSEUM

This book and the exhibition it accompanies
has been supported by the Countryside Commission

A further donation has been received
from The Associates of the V&A

ISBN 0 905209 96 6
Published by
The Victoria and Albert Museum 1984

Designed by Grant Morrison
and Marion Dalley
Printed by Precision Press London

CONTENTS

Front cover: Robert Hills
Skelwith Force
Back cover: James Durden
Summer in Cumberland

○ Denotes colour illustration

FOREWORD

This exhibition is a successor to the series inaugurated in 1974 with *The Destruction of the Country House*. The latter was succeeded by *Change and Decay. The Future of our Churches* in 1977 and *The Garden* in 1979. Each made its point admirably and contributed, I hope, to extending responsibility for the preservation of the historic environment across a far wider spectrum of the community. One can measure their success, for example, in the country house cult, in campaigns to preserve churches or in the burgeoning of garden history as a serious academic discipline. Exhibitions of this type embody the Museum as a vehicle for polemic. *The Discovery of the Lake District* takes one aspect of a theme that was at one time considered for a major heritage exhibition in sequence to the others, on the British Landscape and its fate. In many ways the point is more forcefully made by homing in on one legendary section of our countryside which has been celebrated by pen and brush for over two hundred years. May I thank all those who have made this possible.

Roy Strong Director July 1984

PREFACE

Over the years the Victoria and Albert Museum has organised events, exhibitions and seminars, which have highlighted the effects of a changing historical environment on some of the most valued monuments of our collective heritage. The future of urban churches, the monuments of faith and evangelism in the nineteenth century, and of country houses, the very symbols of our oligarchy, had seemed uncertain in a modern polity organising itself for secular humanism and democracy. Around these monuments, controversy could hardly be said to exist: on whatever view of the historical process, conservation of the material culture was clearly a general social duty, one in which we might be failing, but which we at least acknowledged. Religious and political controversy had moved on, and the problem was a relatively simple one of resources and techniques.

The Discovery of the Lake District, which we have developed and expanded from two earlier exhibitions organised by the Dove Cottage Trust in Grasmere, has much in common with its predecessors at the Victoria and Albert Museum. Everyone agrees that the countryside is a good thing, and that in a special moral sense it belongs to everyone: that it needs care and conservation, and that public resources are required to support it. What is different about the countryside now is that it may just be beginning to be really controversial. Somewhere on the fringes of political consciousness, in an uneasy trap between the chauvinist politics of European agriculture and the agonising problems of real rural communities, is possibly emerging a major confrontation of interest, similar to that which characterised politically the century of agrarian reform before Peel's abolition of the Corn Laws in 1846.

In organising the present show we have deliberately courted awareness of this background, and have invited the Countryside Commission to participate, not just as financiers, but as the official inheritors of the aesthetic authority and responsibility for the landscape which the exhibition traces out. Any student of the subject quickly becomes aware that the aesthetics of landscape have always been profoundly political and economic: the basic categories and terminology of the subject, concepts such as the Pastoral, Arcadianism, the Beautiful (in Edmund Burke's definition) belong in a structure of ancient axioms that identify human happiness with the sunny productivity of the land. It is no accident that 'classical' landscape in England – the neo-Claudian paintings of Richard Wilson and the tradition of garden design from Capability Brown to Humphry Repton – belong precisely to that century of agrarian economic dominance that Peel foreclosed. The Picturesque revolution of the 1790's found metaphors and political significance in the dislike of levelling, in the preference for inequality and variety, and for the preservation of the time honoured, in the landscape as in society at large. The classical Whig landscape, the great house surrounded by a glacis of shaven lawns, isolated from its offices and other signs of belonging in an organic system of economic and moral dependencies, was to the theoreticians of the Tory Picturesque a sort of parable of events in Revolutionary France. The economic and patriotic reasons for planting woods in wastelands were emphasised by the same writers during the war; and afterwards, in the recession of the mid 1820's which was itself partly a function of excessively high food prices and of the pauperisation of the working class, it was an aesthetically generated sense of *noblesse oblige* among the Tory landowners that led to large scale schemes of land drainage and planting: morally, economically and aesthetically investment to counter the recession seemed right.

These matters interest me, and they seem to arise at every turn of the history contained in the following pages. I hope this is so for everyone, for I hope also that this side of the subject has not been over emphasised, and with its lack of stridency will not be overlooked. In bringing the subject up to date, beyond the apparent watershed of 1850, we have drawn out the continuities and tried to show how the problems and conflicts of the present have a natural history which can help in their resolution. For us here, as for the colleagues in Grasmere who have contributed so much to this show, the first object is to lay out the subject as a fairly factual narrative, so that a general knowledge of what has happened in the past may lead to a more informed public debate about the future. Too often those concerned with the landscape take up a prohibitory stance and appear to discourage people from visiting places: too often, as in the case of Wordsworth's opposition to the railway at Windermere, the point is taken that public access is unwanted by those already in residence. What I hope comes across clearly in this exhibition is that historically the problem has always been one of opening the place up, of showing the sanctum properly: that West, Gilpin, Wordsworth, the National Trust and the Countryside Commission belong in a continuity of humanely inclusive values. For a museum in London the problem is directly analogous to our familiar one of caring for and publicising the national heritage of works of art. The view of the Lake District as itself a work of human art, accumulative of the riches brought to it by two and a half centuries of physical development, of writing, painting and personal self exploration and exercise, is what we have most wanted to make clear. If the exhibition is at all about Nature, it is about Nature as a construct of the human mind.

ACKNOWLEDGEMENTS

Many people have helped, and some have been so vital in the enterprise that it would hardly be right merely to say that they helped. Robert Woof and Peter Bicknell are obviously in that category, with Graham Coggins, and if thanks are wanted they are certainly due, both to the individuals and to the institutions whose resources they each in a sense delivered: Robert Woof and the Dove Cottage Trust, Peter Bicknell and his great collection of Lake District books at Kings College Cambridge, and Graham Coggins with his colleagues at the Countryside Commission. Interest and support have similarly been generously given by Lawrence Harwood and the National Trust, the Lake District Special Planning Board, the North West Water Authority, the Outward Bound Trust, the Alpine Club, the Fell and Rock Club, the Youth Hostel Association, the Calvert Trust for the Disabled, St. Anne's School Windermere and the Leverhulme Trust.

Without the scholarly support of Julian Treuherz at the Manchester City Art Gallery and Francis Hawcroft at the Whitworth, Mary Bennett at Liverpool, Stephen Wildman at Birmingham, David Scrase at Cambridge, Kenneth Garlick at Oxford, Christopher Gilbert at Leeds Mary Burkett and Vicky Slowe at Kendal, Bruce Hanson and the Brantwood Educational Trust and John Dawson at the Ruskin Museum in Coniston; without generous loans from the British Museum and the Tate Gallery, the exhibition would hardly have existed. To Lord Rochdale, Mr Derek Lockett, David Nicholson, Jake and Joran Nicholson and Kate Nicholson, to Kathleen Raine and Sidney Cross, and to all the lenders, especially perhaps those private individuals who remain modestly anonymous, thanks are due. To Agnews, Spinks, the Christopher Wood Gallery, to Christopher Newall, Miklos Rajnai, James Miller, Henry Wemyss, thanks for loans, scholarly advice and access to records. To the colleagues at the Victoria and Albert Museum, to Michael Kauffmann (as ever) and Lionel Lambourne, Mark Haworth Booth, Anne Buddle, Julian Litten, Chris Titterington and Howard Coutts; to Ronald Lightbown and Ann Hobbs who briefed me on Beatrix Potter, and Jennifer Blain who could cope with Arthur Ransome; to Sally Chappell, Julie Laird, Simon Tait, Garth Hall, Michael Martin and Geoff Opie, for all their specialist help. To the photographers David Lyons and Robert Thrift, and to Geoffrey Berry of the Friends of the Lake District, for the work they have done, and to Brian Coe of the Kodak Museum for learned and enthusiastic advice on historic photographs; to Roger Taylor for the same and for very much else as well; to Geoffrey Beard, for his brilliant and in these pages otherwise unacknowledged booklet *The Greater House in Cumbria,* and to G. H. Pattinson for his privately printed book on his family firm, the builders of Windermere; to Charles Rhyne for an unreasonably generous response to questions about Constable; to Marcia Pointon, for a conversation also about Constable; to Hugh Torrens for an authoritative word on Peter Crosthwaite; to John Nicol, for advice that I hardly know how to characterise but would not have been without; and to scholars generally whose work one treats as common property, like Erwin Panofsky, for his seminal essay 'Et in Arcadia Ego' (*Philosophy and History, essays presented to Ernst Cassirer,* Oxford 1936).

Grant Morrison has designed the catalogue; Isobel Gillan took on the graphics for the exhibition itself. To them, to a typist and to Sara Rodgers who helped me with the illustrations for this book, many thanks.

John Murdoch   June 1984

ARCADIA

A country in the centre of the Peloponnesus, bounded on the north by Achaia, on the west by Elis, on the east by Argolis, and on the south by Laconia and Messinia. It was very mountainous, though, at the same time, diversified with fruitful valleys, and well watered by an abundance of streams. The Arcadians were for the most part shepherds; hence their love of music, and hence also the worship of Pan, as the tutelary deity of the land. They were brave and warlike … Arcadia was anciently called *Drymotis* … owing to its producing such a number of oaks. The Arcadians had settled in the country from such an early period, as to induce them to boast of their having sprung from the earth, and of their being older than the moon.
(J. Lempriere, Bibliotheca Classica … Reading 1788)

Theocritus and the Greek pastoral poets had in fact favoured Sicily as the site of their bucolics, and it was the Latin poets, especially Ovid and Virgil, who set their pastorals in Arcadia and established it as a visionary realm of pastoral innocence in the vanished Golden Age. In Virgil, Arcadia became a psychological rather than a topographical reality, and post-classical Latin poets located it freely, outside Rome on the supposed site of Horace's villa or as in Petrarch in the hills about Avignon. Boccaccio had it near Cortona in Tuscany, the Medici court poets celebrated Fiesole, while for Tasso, Arcadia was everything that life in the modern Italian state, with its burdens of culture and consciousness, could not be. The *Arcadia* (1590) of Philip Sidney on the other hand was in Greece, but for him and for the Elizabethan court the Arcadian landscape was complementary to the many-sided vision of the Queen as Astraea, whose accession to the throne signalled the return of the Golden Age. Arcadianism and the pastoral in England tend to have a close connection with moments of heightened national self-consciousness.

In the seventeenth century, drawing directly on the Virgilian and Ovidian tradition, painters working in Rome endowed the Arcadian pastoral with its characteristic visual embodiments. The early Claude images tend to emphasize the literally pastoral aspect, with staffage of shepherds, goats and cattle (a) rather than the Ovidian gods and mythic beasts of the later pictures (b).

A strain of mutability, present in the tradition since the Theocritan laments over the death of Daphnis, the threat of death and bereavement in the midst of happiness, is occasionally explicit, as in the *locus classicus* of

Arcadianism, Nicholas Poussin's *Et in Arcadia ego* (c. 1630–35) in the Louvre. The tomb on which the shepherds trace out the cryptic letters of the *memento* is an architectural, classicised version of the shocking skull that disrupts the pastoral innocence of the shepherds in the earlier Guercino treatment of the subject (c. 1621–3 Rome, Galleria Corsini).

(b)

Whether ruined or not, the presence of architecture in the landscape testifies generally to the classical civilisation that produced it, and diffuses the implicit threat of death into a sense of the transience even of the most ageless human works. Goethe, confronting the ruined civilisation of Italy on his blissful journey of 1786-8, used the motto 'Auch ich in Arkadien' to characterise his complicated sense of alienation from perfect happiness, a happiness that for him could be symbolised in the classic landscapes of the Italian Arcady.

So often the spokesman for his generation, Goethe may stand as representative of the English tourists who visited Rome in the second half of the eighteenth century, and brought back with them paintings by the seventeenth century masters to furnish their Palladian houses in the English countryside. Cut off from the continent and from the external sources of their culture by the Revolutionary Wars, and participating in the Romantic belief that the finest springs of the common culture lay within the boundaries of the nation state, the English ruling class transferred their Arcady to Britain. They found that the existing literature and imagery of the Lake District already identified the mountains and well watered valleys, clothed in oak woods and given over to the herding of sheep and cattle, with the classical landscapes of the Italian tradition, of Claude, Salvator and the ambiguous figure of 'Poussin'. The Englishman's Arcadia, the Paradise which it was the human condition to yearn for, was discovered.

(a) CLAUDE LORRAIN 1600–82
o Pastoral Landscape with Piping Figures c. 1630–40
    Oil on canvas 99.7 x 133.3 cm.
    Thomas Agnew and Sons Limited
The buildings appear to be an adaption of the Temple of Vesta at Tivoli.

(b) Landscape with Apollo Guarding the Herds of Admetus (Ovid, Metamorphoses Bk. I) 1654
    Oil on canvas 74 x 98 cm.
    Viscount Coke and the Trustees of the Holkham Estate; photograph by courtesy of Thomas Agnew and Sons Limited

THE CLASSIC IMAGE
OF THE LAKES

The tradition of enthusiasm for the scenery of the Lake District was thus founded in the mid eighteenth century on descriptions in words and pictures by visitors who, lacking a strong native tradition of landscape art and being well educated in Latin and Greek, used analogies from the classics to dignify and characterise their scenery. The famous passage from Dr John Brown's letter to Lord Lyttelton:

'the full perfection of KESWICK consists of three circumstances, *Beauty, Horror,* and *Immensity,* united; . . . to give you a complete idea of these three perfections, as they are joined in KESWICK, would require the united powers of *Claude, Salvator,* and *Poussin*'

explicitly points to the classical landscape tradition of seventeenth century Rome, with its strong Ovidian and Virgilian interests, as the means of understanding the qualities found in the Lake District. All the early guides and authorities drew on this tradition both to validate the claim of the landscape to serious attention, and to communicate effectively with the small élite audience that they expected to have.

I

WILLIAM BELLERS fl. 1750-73
1 A View of Derwentwater towards
   Borrowdale 1752
   Engraving, J.B.C. Chatelain and
   S.F. Ravenet, platemark
   36.7 x 53.4 cm.
   King's College Cambridge
   Bicknell Collection

Bellers visited the Lake District in 1751 or 1752, and in the next two years published six prints of the Lakes. Derwentwater was the first. Surrounded by wooded hills and oaks of the Arcadian myths, the lake had something of the appearance of the lakes outside Rome in the Alban Hills. It exemplified a type of landscape which was circular, and included the onlooker's own viewpoint as in an amphitheatre.

THOMAS SMITH of Derby d. 1767
2 View of Derwentwater from Crow
   Park 1767 (first published 1761)
   Engraving, platemark 39 x 55 cm.
   King's College Cambridge
   Bicknell Collection

3 View of Windermere 1767 (first
   published 1761)
   Engraving, platemark 39 x 55 cm.
   King's College Cambridge
   Bicknell Collection

Smith probably visited the Lakes at about the same time as Bellers. His view of Derwentwater, taken from an elevated viewpoint, meets the problem of representing an amphitheatrical landscape more successfully, and differentiates the special circular, enclosed quality of its subject from that of Windermere, which, being long and thin, invites a view of it stretched out in deep perspective, as a prospect. Like Derwentwater, Windermere was from the start recognised as an Arcadian landscape, perhaps more purely so from the pastoral quality of its relatively gentle wooded hills in the lower reaches.

Smith's *Derwentwater* shows almost incidentally the effects of timber cutting on the landscape. After the rising of 1715, the Jacobite third Earl of Derwentwater was executed and his estates passed to Greenwich Hospital. The trees were sold and felled, so that when the idea of Derwentwater with its oaks as an Arcadian landscape became formed within the culture, the sense of outrage and of beauty as vulnerable and transient, was already fundamental to the appreciation of the landscape.

JOHN DALTON 1709-63

4   A Descriptive Poem, addressed to
    Two Ladies, at their return
    from Viewing the Mines
    near Whitehaven
    London 1755
    Trustees of Dove Cottage

Dalton was a Cumbrian, writing here to the daughters of the pre-eminent local family, the owners of the mines and of important 'country houses' within what was already regarded by the local families as a place of resort and renewal. The Lake District as a cultural object was not the invention of outsiders, but was to a great extent a projection from within of its own resources and aesthetic self-consciousness. Dalton thus contrasts the Lowther family mines at Whitehaven with the silvan Arcadian charms of their country estate, and, turning to the landscapes of Borrowdale, coins the famous lines:'

'Horrors like these at first alarm,
But soon with savage grandeur charm
And Raise to noblest thought the mind.'

Published in 1755, Dalton's strict correlation of phenomena with effects belongs within the same aesthetic system as that codified with professional philosophical rigour by Edmund Burke in the Analytical Enquiry of 1757. Learned topographical notes to the Poem were supplied by Sir William Brownrigg, of Ormathwaite under Skiddaw.

JOHN BROWN 1715-66

5   A Description of the
    Lake at Keswick
    Newcastle 1767
    The Master and Fellows of Trinity
    College Cambridge

A Cumbrian both by upbringing and attachment, Brown was a fellow of St John's College Cambridge and a close friend of the Gilpin family (see no. 12). His letter probably written in 1753 to Lord Lyttelton was the earliest document of the classicising cult of the Lake District, but it was not published until part of it appeared in the London Chronicle of 24-26 April 1766, and separately as a pamphlet, five times between 1767 (as here) and 1772.

3

West was the doyen of the Lake District guides, the inventor of the way of looking at landscape from certain pre-ordained viewpoints or Stations so that the experience of tourism, instead of a jumble of impressions, should be a series of properly composed and memorable tableaux. He promoted the static, pictorial sense of landscape and his Stations codified the amphitheatres and prospects of the classic Lake District tour.

Born and educated in Scotland, he was a Jesuit, trained at the English College in Liège, and chaplain at Titcup Hall near Dalton-in-Furness from the early 1760's. To compensate perhaps for this slightly external relation to mainstream English-Protestant society, West's work had a strong tincture of patriotism. Approaching the cult of landscape as a scholar and historian trained on the continent, he was especially conscious of the Englishness of the Lake District, and at the same time insistent on its equality at least with Italian and Swiss paradigms. In the later editions of his Guide, the sense of Windermere and Derwentwater as analogous to classic landscape became an actual process of assimilation, as William Cockin, West's editor, recommended even the building of a city on Windermere to make it more like Geneva.

Around West therefore in the 1770's and 1780's coalesced an interventionist aesthetic, still anxious on the one hand that timber felling should not lessen the silvan charm of the Lakes, but convinced that buildings of suitable form in conspicuous places would improve and adorn the landscape.

THOMAS WEST
6 The Antiquities of Furness
London 1774
Private Collection

West's first book, written after his return to Cumbria. Furness Abbey was the most distinguished local antiquarian monument, and it brought visitors to the Lake District independently of the cult of landscape. West's book, though it contained a 'Descriptive View' of High Furness, with the lakes of Coniston, Esthwaite and Windermere, did not foreshadow in either analysis or enthusiasm the landscape passages of the Guide.

Furness Abbey Francis Frith series no. 3634

7 A Guide to the Lakes: Dedicated to the Lovers of Landscape Studies and to all who have Visited, or intend to Visit the Lakes in Cumberland, Westmorland and Lancashire By the Author of the Antiquities of Furness London and Kendal 1778 Trustees of Dove Cottage

The Guide was the first, and for nearly half a century the most influential guide to the Lakes.

'The design ... is to encourage the taste of visiting the Lakes, by furnishing the traveller with a Guide; and for that purpose are here

collected and laid before him, all the select stations, and points of view noticed by those who have made the tour of the lakes.'
The Stations are:

ON DERWENTWATER
(1) Cockshut Hill Between Keswick and Fiar's Crag ⅛ mile from shore
(2) Crow Park ¼ mile N.W. of second Station
(3) East shore On Barrow Common ½ mile S. of Barrow Cascade House
(4) Top of Castle Crag In Borrowdale 1 mile S. of head of lake
(5) Swinside Hill ¼ mile W. of foot of lake ½ mile S. of Portinscale
(6) Summit of Fawe Park ¼ mile S.E. of fifth Station near Lord Gordon's house
(7) Top of Latrigg 1 mile N.E. of Keswick
(8) Vicarage Garden ½ mile S. of Crosthwaite Church

ON WINDERMERE
(1) West shore Claife Heights near Ferry
(2) On Belle Isle S. Side
(3) On Belle Isle N. Side
(4) West shore On Rawlinson's Nab 4 miles from foot of lake
(5) East shore 1 mile E. of Ferry Point near Golf Course

ON CONISTON
(1) East shore ½ mile N.E. of High Nibthwaite
(2) East shore 1½ miles from foot of lake near Peel Island
(3) East shore 2 miles from head of lake
(4) In centre of lake opposite Coniston Hall and Brantwood

ON BASSENTHWAITE
(1) Armathwaite Hall Near foot of lake, ⅕ mile N. of shore
(2) East shore 'extremity of the promontary' near Scarness 1 mile from foot of lake

(3) East shore Bradness (Broadness) ⅔ mile S. of second Station
(4) West shore near Beck-Wythop 1½ miles from head of lake

N.B. No stations for other lakes described in the Guide

8   A Guide to the Lakes
     London and Kendal 1780
     the second edition
     King's College Cambridge
     Bicknell Collection

West died on 10 July 1779, and his immensely successful publication was taken over by William Cockin (1736-1807), a scholar and schoolmaster of Kendal, who expanded the text, broadening and deepening the stream of aesthetic response, and building into it a freight of poetic allusion. In ten formal Addenda he reprinted much of the earlier Lake District writing, including Brown and Dalton, and especially Thomas Gray's Journal which had itself acquired by this time a sort of classic status (see no. 9).

Cockin, as distinct from West, did much to justify and encourage the development of Arcadian villa schemes in the Lakes, including specific recommendations for the architectural forms suitable for the situation and use as summer houses. Responding to the new circular house and its accompaniments on Belle Isle, he wrote:
> 'I cannot but think them a considerable accession to the beauties of the lake. And could one with a wish throw a bridge from shore to shore, and place the uncommon row of houses near Shap across the island, or even conjure a city upon it ... (it) might then become a rival to the celebrated lake of Geneva, which owes its principal superiority over all other lakes to its having a city at one end and being surrounded with palaces.'

THOMAS GRAY 1716-71

9 The Poems of Mr Gray
To which are prefixed Memoirs of
his Life and Writings
by W. Mason M.A.
York 1775
King's College Cambridge

Gray visited the Lakes in the autumn of
1769 and his letters to Dr. Wharton were
the first literary testament, by an
important professional writer, to the
special aesthetic quality of the district.
The letters were authoritatively edited
by Mason to form a continuous
'journal', and Gray's text, seminal to the
whole subsequent history of Lake
District response, is usually therefore
referred to, though misleadingly, as
the *Journal*.

Apart from his extremist record of
the effect of the Burkean stimulus to
Terror in the Sublime landscape of
Borrowdale:

'Soon after we came under
Gowdar-Crag, a hill more
formidable to the eye, and to the
apprehension, than that of
Lowdore; the rocks at top
deep-cloven perpendicularly by the
rains, hanging loose and nodding
forwards, seen just starting from
their base in shivers. The whole way
down, and the road on both sides, is
strewed with piles of the fragments,
strangely thrown across each other,
and of a dreadful bulk; the place
reminds me of those passes in the
Alps, where the guides tell you to
move with speed, and say nothing,
lest the agitation of the air should
loosen the snows above, and bring
down a mass that would overwhelm
a caravan. I took their counsel here
and hastened on in silence.' *Non
ragioniam di lor, ma, guarda, e passa.*

the *Journal* established Grasmere for the
first time in the Arcadian canon of Lake
District landscapes. Gray's deeply
imbued Miltonic consciousness,
however, seeks out the Paradisal

metaphor, and makes wonderfully
explicit the late eighteenth century
equation between the cottage and its
surroundings, and the Garden of Eden.
The contrast, also, between the
rightness of the modest cottage and the
'flaring' gentleman's house, exactly
anticipates Wordsworth and the
doctrines of the high Picturesque
aesthetes after 1794.

'Not a single red tile, no flaring
gentleman's house or garden wall
breaks in upon the repose of this
little unsuspected paradise; but all is
peace, rusticity, and happy poverty,
in its neatest and most becoming
attire'.

THOMAS WALMSLEY 1763-1805/6

10 Bowness on Windermere 1808
Coloured aquatint, Jukes and
Sargent, platemark
36.5 x 45.5 cm.
King's College Cambridge
Bicknell Collection

JOHN 'WARWICK' SMITH
AND JOHN EMES

11 Sixteen Views of the Lakes in
Cumberland and Westmorland
S. Alken, imprints 1794, 1795;
issued without text or title to be
bound with West's *Guide*
Stock-gill Force, near
Ambleside, 1794
Aquatint, cut within the platemark
in binding; shown bound in West's
Guide, seventh edition 1799
Peter Bicknell

Views by all these artists were advertised
in the later editions of West's *Guide*, and
in that sense belong closely to the
aesthetic promoted by West's editors.
Walmsley especially 'intervenes' in the
topography of Bowness Church and the
round house on Belle Isle to improve the
view, in the spirit of William Cockin. A
similar view of Bowness, in gouache, by
Walmsley is in the Victoria and Albert
Museum, much deteriorated.

WILLIAM GILPIN
1724-1804

Another Cumbrian, Gilpin was in a sense advertising his own in bringing tourists in even greater numbers to the Lake District after the publication in 1786 of his *Observations*. His original work now in the Bodleian Library had circulated for many years in manuscript, bound in eight volumes with some two hundred illustrations, sketch maps and descriptive panoramas (by the author, his brother Sawrey, Gilpin, John Warwick Smith and others), and attained its greatest influence amongst the élite group who read it in that form. Textually, it was stiffer and more pedantic in its printed state, and it led quite rapidly to the onset of a satirical reaction against the specifically 'Gilpinesque' approach to landscape, its obsessive pictorialism and tendency to vagueness and generalisation. Gilpin's topographical imprecision especially led to much immediate criticism, and yet his strength lay precisely in his theoretical interests. For all his imperfections as a writer, and his lack of a proper Burkean rigour in the use of terms, his text shows a consistent interest in the formal problems of a classical landscape discipline, of wider practical usefulness – as perhaps Constable found – than the stereotyping of views implicit in West's approach.

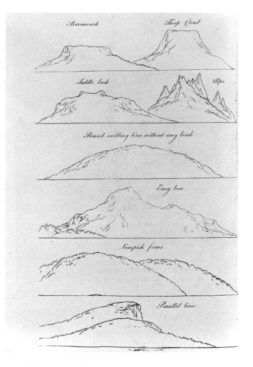

12

WILLIAM GILPIN

12 Observations, relative chiefly to Picturesque Beauty, made in the year 1772, on Several Parts of England; especially the Mountains and Lakes ...

2 volumes London 1786
Trustees of Dove Cottage
The title of Gilpin's book makes clear at least one of its strengths: Gilpin was a brilliant *observer,* both in the sense that he probably intended of making analytical, connected observations, and in a sense that was just beginning to be valued when he published, of recording minute and disjointed effects with particularising vividness. Here he notices the changing weather over Borrowdale, Newlands and Keswick.

'The clouds which were gathering upon the mountains, and sweeping along the vallies, began to interrupt our view. Everything was wrapped in obscurity ... The whole valley of Gascadale smoked like a boiling cauldron; and we got our ideas of it only by catches, as the volumes of clouds dispersed, at intervals, into purer air ... Among the beautiful appearances of fogs, and mists, their *gradually going off* may be observed. A landscape takes a variety of pleasing hues, as it passes, in a retiring fog, through the different degrees of obscurity into full splendour.'

Crosthwaite, born near Keswick, returned there in 1779 after a career in the merchant navy, and opened a museum. His notebooks prove him to have been far from the figure of fun that he is sometimes still reckoned. He was a devoted amateur of natural science, a serious and gifted observer of phenomena in the English empirical tradition; infinitely more flamboyant in person than, but not fundamentally different in mind from, say, Gilbert White of Selborne.

His maps were the first specifically of the Lakes, and represented a formidable achievement both of surveying and of commercial enterprise. They contained, in parallel with successive editions of West's *Guide*, information on the Stations – Crosthwaite added many of his own – and, most interestingly, information on the progress of building development, on the model of Cockin's vision, around the shores. The Crosthwaite maps, decorated with *remarques* of the new houses, stand thus as maps of the Arcadian Lakes.

PETER
CROSTHWAITE
1735-1808

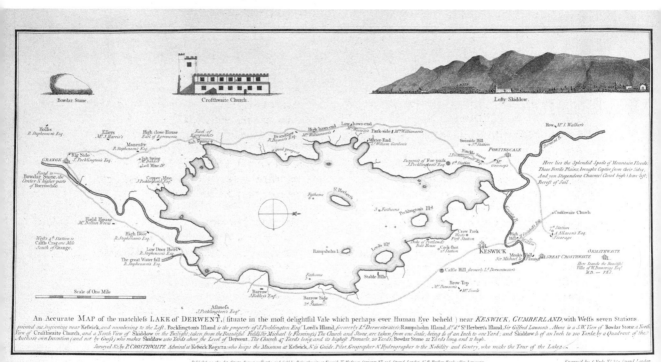

PETER CROSTHWAITE

13   An Accurate Map of the matchless Lake of Derwent (situated in the most delightful Vale which perhaps ever Human Eye beheld) Keswick 10 June 1783 Trustees of Dove Cottage

Crosthwaite was an expert in self-advertisement, referring to himself on this plate as 'Admiral at Keswick Regatta; who keeps the Museum at Keswick, is Guide, Pilot, Geographer, Hydrographer to the Nobility and Gentry, who make the Tour of the Lakes.

T. MARTIN

14 A New and Exact Map of the
Beautiful Vale of Keswick in
Cumberland
28 October 1784
T. Martin, Writing Master surveyed
the beautiful Vale of Keswick and
constructed his map accordingly
The Fitz Park Museum and Art
Gallery Keswick

Crosthwaite had rivals: a rival Museum
which he despised, and evidently rival
map-makers. Martin's map is a
wonderful example of delayed
provincial Rococo, but has none of the
commercial aptitude of Crosthwaite's
and little of the information.

JAMES CLARKE fl. 1775-1800

15 A Survey of the Lakes of
Cumberland, Westmorland
and Lancashire 1787
Trustees of Dove Cottage

Clarke was a Penrith surveyor, and his
maps provided the principal commercial
competition for Crosthwaite's. They
were accompanied by a letterpress
chiefly distinguished as part of the early
reaction against the narrow minded
pictorialism and the absence of hard fact
in most of the writing about the Lake
District. Clarke omits for example
information on West's Stations, and the
illustrations that sometimes were bound
with his text, unlike Gilpin's, are of
particular places, not generalisations
about the character of an area.

Clarke's large elegant folding maps
and itineraries, less crowded with
information, remain easier to read than
the later impressions of Crosthwaite.
Occassionally prints after drawings by
Farington and Smith were bound with
Clarke's *Survey*.

SMITH

16 Smith's Map of the Lakes 1802
(first published 1800)
Folded map in slip case
King's College Cambridge

Bicknell Collection

The earliest pocket map intended
specifically for the tourist. Useful
information is set out in tables on the
face of the map. Five editions were
published up to 1824.

JONATHAN OTLEY 1766-1855

17 New Map of the Lakes 1823
(first published 1818)
Folded map in slip case
King's College Cambridge
Bicknell Collection

An improvement on the type of tourist
map pioneered by Smith, and
superseding it. It remained current in
eight editions until 1850.

18 A Concise Description
of the English Lakes and
Adjacent Mountains
second edition
Keswick 1825
(first published 1823
sixth edition 1837-42)
King's College Cambridge

The first factual and practical guide,
giving information rather than aesthetic
analysis or rhapsody.

STEPHEN PENN fl. c 1733

19 North-east Prospect of the
O Country up Thurston Water from
Peelnears 1733
Watercolour
32.6 x 48.2 cm.
Victoria and Albert Museum
P.3-1941

Thurston Water is Coniston. Penn's
drawing, a brilliant and beautiful record
of a tract of country, is as schematic as a
map and derives from the Netherlandish
tradition of landscape painting, the so
called bird's eye view, which applies a
rigorous perspective from an impossible
viewpoint. It was submerged by the
more naturalistic vision of the classical
landscape tradition, with its true
viewpoint, controlled recession and
aerial or atmospheric perspective.

DISCIPLES OF THOMAS GRAY:
THE EARLY PAINTERS

Born at Leigh in Lancashire, Farington returned to the Lake District in 1775, perhaps inspired by the recent publication of Gray's *Journals,* and worked for several seasons on drawings that were engraved in *Views of the Lakes* (1783), *Britannia Depicta,* Part IV (1816) and *The Lakes Delineated* (1816). In 1790 he compiled a set of views (now in the British Art Center, New Haven) of the the sites visited by Gray, arranged by his own hand, in apparently simple homage to the master.

   He worked in a landscape that had already been 'discovered' at least in a literary sense. There is evidence that he responded, particularly to begin with, to the parts – Keswick, Grasmere – characterised by Gray as paradisal. The paradisal scene thus gave him the entrée to the Lake District aesthetic.

JOSEPH FARINGTON
1747-1821

2

JOSEPH FARINGTON
20 Wast-dale Head, near Wast Water in
     Cumberland August 1781
     Pencil, pen and ink and wash
     overall 25.2 x 32.5 cm.
     Birmingham Museum
     and Art Gallery
Engraved by J. Landsern for *The Lakes...delineated, 1816*

21 Twenty Views of the Lakes
     2 volumes London 1784-9
     The Lower Waterfall at Rydal
     Engraved by B.T. Pouncey
     platemark 25.5 x 36.8 cm.
     King's College Cambridge
     Bicknell Collection
The description of the plates in English and French was almost certainly supplied by Wordsworth's uncle, William Cookson.

THOMAS HEARNE 1744-1817
22 Sir George Beaumont and Joseph
     Farington Sketching a Waterfall
     probably 1777
     Watercolour 44.5 x 29.2 cm.
     Trustees of Dove Cottage
Hearne and Farington were in the Lake District together in the Summer of 1777, almost certainly at the invitation of their patron Sir George Beaumont. This

23

drawing appears to commemorate the presence of the three of them probably at the falls of Lodore above Derwentwater. The three stayed at the inn beside Lodore. The precedents, both for Hearne's drawing of the artists at work, and for the choice by the artists of a close-up view of the falls, lie in Rome and its surroundings, particularly in the work of artists at Tivoli.

23 Sir George Beaumont and Joseph Farington sketching in oils c. 1777 Sketch, associated with the above Pencil 17.8 x 19.1 cm. Trustees of Dove Cottage

24 Derwentwater from Skiddaw Watercolour over pencil 18.7 x 27 cm.

Leeds City Art Gallery A view of the Derwentwater amphitheatre, almost in the round, taken from much higher up than the Crow Park images.

25 Derwentwater from Brandelhow Woods Watercolour over pencil 20.5 x 30.5 cm. Trustees of the Tate Gallery A 'prospect' across Derwentwater, towards the relatively open and parklike north end of the lake.

26 Remains of the Chapter House of Furness Abbey 1777 Pen, ink, grey and brown wash 18 x 25 cm. Walker Art Gallery Liverpool

27 Panorama of Derwentwater from
    Crow Park
    Pen and wash, six sheets joined
    25.1 x 233.6 cm.
    Victoria and Albert Museum
According to Southey, when
Beaumont, Farington and Hearne were
together in the Lake District in 1777, the
year before Sir George's marriage,
Hearne 'made for him a sketch of the
whole circle of his vale, from a field
called Crow Park. Sir George intended
to build a circular banqueting room, and
have this painted round the walls. If the
execution had not always been
procrastinated, here would have been
the first panorama. I have seen the
sketch, now preserved on a roll more
than twenty feet in length.' *(Life and*

*Correspondence, ed. CC. Southey, 1850,
VI, 215)*
    Hearne's panorama is now lost; had it
been completed, it would indeed have
been the first panorama, antedating
Robert Barker's Edinburgh panorama
by more than fifteen years, and, as a
highly original decorative scheme, close
in date to William Lock's commission
for the drawing room at Norbury Park.
Hearne's lost sketch therefore was
absolutely at the forefront of
developments in British painting
at this time.
    The Victoria and Albert Museum
panorama has been attributed to the
amateur Christopher Machell
(1747-1827), having shared a Machell
family provenance along with other

28

cartoon that Southey saw, worked over by another hand, is a matter for judgement. Certainly the quality of the draughtsmanship is spiky and hesitant. Yet minimally, these sheets should stand as the closest likely record of what the Hearne-Beaumont panorama might have been, taking the incomplete amphitheatrical view the vital step further, and projecting it into the full enveloping circle.

CHRISTOPHER MACHELL 1747–1827
Attributed to
28 Hawes Water, near Shap
Westmorland
October 4 1779
Pen, ink and watercolour
39.1 x 57.7 cm.
Victoria and Albert Museum

The view is southward from the delta of Measandbank (submerged since the raising of the water level by Manchester Corporation).

Machell has the honour of the attribution of the parcel of drawings distributed from a family provenance between the Victoria and Albert Museum, the Walker Art Gallery and Abbot Hall. The drawings that I have examined seem to be by a variety of hands, some very similar to the hands of masters known to have been working in the Lake District during the 1770's and 1780's. Apart from Hearne, with whom the panorama is in some degree associable, the leading candidate must be Farington. Machell, a military man and therefore likely to have had the normal soldier's training in basic draughtsmanship, is believed to have had commitments in North America during the War of Independence, and his diary places his return to the family domain some time after 1786. The majority of the Victoria and Albert Museum drawings date from 1789, but this sheet, unmistakably dated October 1779, is especially difficult to accept as by Machell.

highly accomplished drawings, stylistically very close to Farington (see for example no. 28), and a much cruder group now at Abbot Hall, all thus reckoned to be by Machell. The panorama is datable on internal evidence, the costumes and the state of tree growth, to the mid 1770's. It would be astonishing if an amateur, even a brilliant metropolitan amateur like Sir George Beaumont, had been able at this time to produce a panorama. The intellectual effort and stern graphic discipline required should be the hall marks of the academically trained professional artist.

Whether the Victoria and Albert Museum sheets can be accepted as by Hearne, as perhaps sketches for the

Beaumont was the outstanding personality who came to the Lake District from outside (from Leicestershire and London) and contributed seminally to its developing culture in the last quarter of the eighteenth century. A pupil himself of Richard Wilson, the friend and patron of Farington and Hearne, he helped to bring into the Lake District the developed resources of London classicism, and to build up with his patronage the corpus of available prints and exhibited pictures that dealt with the unspoiled Paradise described by Thomas Gray. Beaumont's own development over the years parallels changes in the cultural environment, from Wilson–Arcadian classicism, he particpated with his friend and correspondent Uvedale Price in the developments in taste of the 1790's, taking into the heart of English aesthetics some of the lessons in close-focus, high horizon landscape of the Dutch and Flemish traditions.

Farington records him, in 1797, painting with a Hobbema and a Rubens in front of him for guidance and inspiration. By about 1810 or soon after, perhaps responding to the same stimuli from the culture as Constable was, he had begun sketching in oils, as it were out of doors, to record the immediacy of effects in the changing face of nature, with the brilliant rapidity of technique aimed at by the high Romantic artists. And at the same time, he was the friend, patron and correspondent of Wordsworth for thirty years, Wordsworth's main point of contact with the world of professional painters and the visually cultivated.

SIR GEORGE BEAUMONT
29 Derwentwater c. 1798
Oil on millboard 38.5 x 54 cm.
Leicester City Art Gallery

30 Waterfall at Keswick c. 1803
Black chalk and wash, 31 x 27.9 cm.
Trustees of the Tate Gallery
On the original backing board is the inscription: "G.H. Beaumont Keswick August 11 1803 – ". It was one of two drawings left at Greta Hall at the end of Beaumont's stay with Coleridge's landlord, Mr. William Jackson in the summer of 1803.

Coleridge told Beaumont that he had wept when he saw the drawings:
> It will give a lasting Interest to the Drawings of the Waterfall, that I first saw it through tears. I was indeed unwell and sadly nervous; and I must not be ashamed to confess to you, my honoured Friends! That I found a bodily relief in weeping, and yielded to it.

29

31 Derwentwater 1807
Oil on millboard 20.5 x 30.5 cm.
Leicester City Art Gallery

32 Keswick Lake
Oil on millboard 24.5 x 30.5 cm.
Leicester City Art Gallery

ANTHONY DEVIS 1729–1817
33 Derwentwater and Skiddaw from
O   Lord's Island
Oil on canvas 114 x 138.5 cm.
Abbot Hall Art Gallery Kendal

30

REACTION IN THE 1790's

Already in 1787 Clarke's *Survey of the Lakes* had shown the commonsense impatience of many people, including tourists, with the extravagant language and obsessive pictorialism of Lake District enthusiasts. The publication of William Gilpin's *Observations* provided the clearest example of dogmatism, and the ludicrous side of the business – the countryside crawling with upper class tourists all busy mounting elevated Stations, and chattering loosely about the prospect – began to be evident. In the 1790's, with the publication of Uvedale Price's *Essays on the Picturesque* (Hereford 1794, and successive editions in London), there was evidence of a return to the strictness of aesthetic discourse that Edmund Burke had attempted to impose in his *Enquiry into the Sublime and the Beautiful* of 1757. Unlike Gilpin, who wrote indifferently of Picturesque Beauty, Price discriminated between the sensory qualities of the Beautiful and the Picturesque, and discerned in the latter the possibility of a new aesthetic based on appreciation of the way things grew naturally through time and benign neglect, in the landscape as in society at large. Attacking the school of classical 'improvers', he pointed out that houses stuck up on eminences above shaven lawns, with a few trees dotted about to emphasise the greatness of the Prospect, worked a sort of autocratic violence in Nature, and that the cult of Prospects in general diverted attention from what was close to the eye, and was indeed far richer and more rewarding to study than what the mind could imagine for itself.

In the summers of 1796-97 and 99, the Reverend James Plumptre, a Fellow of Clare College, Cambridge, made three long walking tours in the Lakes. In 1797 he recorded in his diary that he 'Read Price on the Picturesque'. He was already working on a satirical play, *The Lakers* (the only known copies of which are in the British Library and Cambridge University Library), which anticipated by several years the similar satires of Jane Austen and Thomas Love Peacock, and of William Combe and Thomas Rowlandson.

THOMAS ROWLANDSON 1756-1827

34 Dr. Syntax Sketching the Lake
O Drawn and etched by Rowlandson
coloured by another hand
Trimmed within the platemark
work area 10.8 x 18.3 cm.
Plate 16 of 'Dr Syntax's Tour to the
Lakes', *The Tour of Dr Syntax in
Search of the Picturesque, A Poem*,
third edition, Ackermann, London
1813 Victoria and Albert Museum
Library Dyce 2412

The letterpress, produced after
Rowlandson's drawings, was by
William Combe (1741-1823). Syntax at
last reaches Derwentwater:

> Soon as the morn began to break,
> Old Grizzle bore him to the lake;
> Along its banks he gravely pac'd,
> When, lo, a threat'ning storm
> appear'd:
> Phoebus the scene no longer
> cheer'd:
> The dark clouds sink on ev'ry hill:
> The floating mists the valleys fill:
> Nature, transform'd, began to lour,
> And threaten'd a tremendous
> shower.
> "I love", he cry'd, "to hear the rattle,
> When elements content in battle;
> For I insist, though some may flout
> it,
> Who write about it and about it
> [sic],
> That we the *picturesque* may find
> In thunder loud, or whistling
> wind;"

Syntax himself was based on Gilpin, and
the satire takes up shrewdly points that
are indeed specially characteristic of
Gilpin, as here Gilpin's interest in the
drama of changing weather (see no. 12).
The satire is affectionate and represents
the Doctor in the manner of Fielding's
Parson Adams in *Joseph Andrews*, the
eighteenth century archetype of this
innocent abroad. Like Plumptre,
Rowlandson and Combe recognized in
the Picturesque of Gilpin's generation an
ineffectuality and lack of seriousness and

rigour, which exposed it to laughter but
not contempt. Their work is however
specific in its target, and should not be
understood as a general assault on the
aesthetics of the Picturesque, but rather
as a contribution to the advances in its
doctrine that followed on from Uvedale
Price's *Essays*. As *Syntax* first appeared
in Ackermann's *Poetical Magazine* in
1809, the prints emerging from his busy
Picturesque atelier, its relation to the
contemporary debate would have been
understood by its early readers.

35

35 Sir Henry Morshead felling his
timber to settle his play debts 1816
Watercolour 14.5 x 22.8 cm.
Victoria and Albert Museum
Dyce 795

The subject is actually Sir John
Morshead (1747-1813), the first baronet
of Trennant Park in Cornwall, who sold
his estates between 1807 and 1809 to pay
his gambling debts. Though dated 1816,
Rowlandson's treatment of the subject
should be closer to 1809, the period of
Dr Syntax. Controversy over timber
felling, indeed the passionate opposition
it aroused, had been a constant factor in
the cult of landscape, going back at least
as far as the felling of the Derwentwater
woods (see no. 3). The sense of its
absolute immorality is here contained in
the presentation of tree felling as one of
the fruits of sinful gambling.
Rowlandson and Syntax after all shared
the essential ethics of the Picturesque.

How Gilpin read *The Lakers*, which was never professionally produced on the stage, is not recorded, but Plumptre wrote to him in early 1801, apologising for the implicit disrespect. Gilpin wrote back handsomely, responding to the charge that his view of landscape was cavalier towards Nature and that he unduly exalted the pictorial qualities of composition, light, balance of foreground and distance – 'Nor do we depreciate Nature, but exalt her. With an open hand she gives us corn; but she does not condescend to make a loaf'.

Game to Gilpin; but the match turned inevitably in favour of the Pricean naturalists and conservationists. The essential seriousness of the new Picturesque – its capacity to reflect a view of man's integrated historical relation through time to his environment – provided the developing idiom of British aesthetics in the era of the Napoleonic wars and after. Plumptre's exact contemporary at Cambridge, William Wordsworth was one of the most devastating critics of the 'old' Picturesque, focussing here on the utter triviality of its concerns when compared with the real business of art and poetry – 'Man, Nature and Human Life'.

WILLIAM WORDSWORTH
36   The Brothers
Lyrical Ballads Volume II 1800
These Tourists, Heaven preserve us! needs must live
A profitable life: some glance along,
Rapid and gay, as if the earth were air,
And they were butterflies to wheel about
Long as their summer lasted; some, as wise,
Upon the forehead of a jutting crag. Sit perch'd with book and pencil on their knee,
And look and scribble, scribble on and look,
Until a man might travel twelve stout miles,
Or reap an acre of his neighbour's corn.

'The Brothers' was among the first poems that Wordsworth composed after he came to live at Dove Cottage, Christmas 1799. It is a pastoral poem in the form of a conversation between the parson of Ennerdale and a supposed stranger. The parson, who speaks first, complains of the idle and foolish tourists, who are depicted with notebook and pencil in their hand. These visitors who draw the scene but who fail to recognise the serious and passionate life of the men living in the valley are implicitly censured in the poem. As Wordsworth told Charles James Fox this poem (along with 'Michael') was "written with a view to show that men who do not wear fine cloaths can feel deeply". In his poem, Wordsworth is rejecting the only published commentary on Ennerdale at that date; this is an appendix to West's *Guide to the Lakes* where the artist is urged to take a pencil to "Snatch all the transient colours of the lake"; or, if he can, "Seize, ah! seize on Pillar's lofty top/That passing mist." To Wordsworth, scenery without people, and their lives among it, was of little importance.

THE VILLAS OF ARCADIA

An essential early step in the establishment of the Lake District as a great
landscape on the European model was the provision of a suitable
architectural presence, both to prompt general memories of pictures by
Claude, and to make the Lake District a habitable and festive place, a
landscape of music parties and regattas. The first such improvements
were undertaken by local families, but in the last quarter of the
eighteenth century the great families from the fringes of the Lake District
began to move in, establishing summer houses in their own northern
Arcadia. As the cult grew, the influx was from further afield, until in the
mid nineteenth century the Lake District villa was as accessible from
London as from Manchester. From the beginning, the architectural
improvement of the lakes was carried on with surprising coordination
between the individual owners, whose houses formed an intricate visual
and social system, especially on Windermere, by 1800 the most
developed of the lakes.

38

The first and the finest of the explicitly classical villas built to adorn the
landscape was the circular house on Belle Isle in Windermere, designed
by John Plaw in 1774 for Thomas English. Verses by a local poet,
William Robinson of Kendal, composed in 1773 described the garden,
apparently a design influenced by William Chambers' chinoiserie, and
evidently intended to evoke the ethos of an 'Eden-scene/An Heaven on
Earth, most beautifully wild!'

37 Crosthwaite's Map of Windermere
    (no. 13).

JOHN PLAW c.1745-1820
38 Rural Architecture London 1794
    'The Frontispiece, designed by the
    Author, the figures drawn by Mr.
    Deare, Sculptor at Rome; the
    Landscape by Mr. Barrett.
    Victoria and Albert Museum
    Library
    The subject is Taste, accompanying
    Rural Simplicity, and pointing to
    one of the Most beautiful Scenes this
    County can boast of, viz. The Lake
    Windermere: on the largest Island in
    which is built a circular villa after a
    Design of the Author's.'
    Aquatint by Francis Jukes

THOMAS WHITE
39 Plan of Improvements for Belle Isle
    Watercolour on vellum
    Private Collection
By 1781 Mr. English had run out of
money, and the estate was bought by the
Trustees of the young Isabella Curwen,
the heiress of Worthington Hall, and the
mines of West Cumbria. The island,
previously known as Long Holme, was
re-named in her honour. Thomas White,
a landscape gardener from
Nottinghamshire with a national
reputation, was hired. He stripped out
the chinoiserie and the formal gardens of
the original plan, and produced a design
which, with its perimeter walk, belt of
trees and clumps within, dispersed over
a smooth grassy sward, owed much to
Capability Brown.

JOHN WARWICK SMITH 1749-1831
40 Views of the Lakes in Cumberland
    Five parts, London 1791-5
    Twenty plates by J. Merigot
    Belleisle Lodge 1791
    Etching and aquatint
    platemark 33 x 47 cm.
    King's College Cambridge
    Bicknell Collection

40

This plate and the rest of the series is
dedicated to John Christian Curwen.

41 View of Windermere and Belle Isle
o   showing the house c.1790
    Watercolour
    Private Collection

42 View of Windermere, Bowness and
o   Belle Isle with a man reading on a
    seat on the garden walk 1790
    Watercolour
    Private Collection

43 View of Windermere and Belle Isle
o   with a lady and child on the
    garden walk 1791
    Watercolour
    Private Collection
These are three drawings from a series
still at Belle Isle and presumably
commissioned by John Christian
Curwen directly from Smith to celebrate
this and the other Curwen properties at
Workington. Apparently only one of the
series, a view of the Ferry on
Windermere, corresponds to a print in
the Smith-Merigot series

AMELIA NOWELL fl. c.1795-1804
44 Windermere and Belle Isle
    Watercolour 10.5 x 16.5 cm.
    Trustees of the British Museum

45   Belle Isle as it is today
     Photograph
     David Lyons 1984
Though strongly disliked by Dorothy
Wordsworth when she saw Belle Isle,
and still a raw neologism in June 1802,
by the 1830's the house and garden had
attained some dignity of age. The island
was often let, and Wordsworth referred
to it as 'Borrow me an island' in
flattering reference to the islands in Lake
Maggiore which were, for Pricean
disciples such as he, an object of
emulation. White's achievement in
planting great stands of hardwood
timber has proved to be monumental,
classic and the nearest thing there may
be to a permanent contribution to
the landscape.

46   Storrs Hall
     Photograph
     David Lyons 1984
Built in a green-field site for Sir John
Legard of Ganton Hall, Yorks, Storrs
was thus exceptional in the Lake
District, where the landowners used
traditional manorial powers to restrict
new development until the mid-19th
century. The design of the original box
was standard builder's 'Georgian', but
there is evidence of a response to the
literature in the large double-storey
multi-faceted bay window projecting
from the front of the house, apparently
in emulation of William Cockin's praise
of the octagon for houses at significant
points of the landscape. This is clearly
visible in Mary Dixon's view of
Windermere (no. 47).

     MARY DIXON d. 1820
47   Windermere looking North
o   showing Storrs Hall
     Oil on board
     9.6 x 16.6 cm.
     Private Collection

48   Windermere and Fell Foot
o   Oil on canvas put down on board

8. 5 x 13.2 cm.
     Trustees of Dove Cottage
Fell Foot was demolished in the present
century and the site is now a
'Countryside Park.' The original house
was built for Jeremiah Dixon, a former
Lord Mayor of Leeds. His wife Mary
was the daughter of Joseph Smeaton,
designer of the Eddystone Lighthouse.
She painted this view of the house,
which shows it to have been three
storeys with a curious entrance porch,
its roof resting on slender pillars, facing
southwestward down the lake. When
the Dixons moved from Fell Foot, Mary
wrote that she was leaving her Paradise
behind.

49   The Temple at Storrs
     Photograph
     David Lyons 1984
Designed in 1804 by Joseph Michael
Gandy, the temple to celebrate the
admirals Howe, Duncan, St Vincent and
Nelson, was Sir John Legard's last
building at Storrs. It reflects and
complements across the water the other
octagon, the original Claife Station, and
with Belle Isle, the three developments
make up a coherent classicising group in
this central area of Windermere.

     Storrs, under its next owner, the West
India merchant Colonel John Bolton
(who re-employed Gandy to give the
house its present form) became a centre
of the Windermere festivals and regattas,
elaborate rituals of Regency aristocracy,
wrapping the political élite in
associations of the Virgilian boat race in
Book IV of the *Aeneid*. The high point
was the Regatta of August 1825, when
Canning and Scott coincided at
Windermere, and John Wilson,
journalist ('Christopher North') and
Tory Professor of Moral Philosophy at
Edinburgh, organized the festivities
from his house at Elleray. There was a
champagne dinner, and the next day
fifty oared barges splashed in procession
between the islands.

CLAIFE STATION   The strange edifice, Claife Station, was built in 1799 on the site of West's first 'Station', or viewpoint for the appreciation of Windermere. The Reverend William Braithwaite the absentee rector, somewhat reclusive in temperament, came to live in his native Hawkshead; he participated in the legislation for enclosing the common land of Claife Heights in 1794. It was he who constructed the octagonal building, the "first pleasure house" referred to by Wordsworth, on a model recommended by William Cockin, the first editor of West's *Guide*. That original eight-sided shape is now visible within the ruins of the later structure.

In 1802, ownership of the site passed to the Curwens of Belle Isle. Building continued and the octagon was encased in a rectangular castellated structure, pushed out at the front in a great square bay. Behind the "pleasure house" a curtain wall, with gothic slits and windows was developed to give more apparent mass to the building when seen from a distance. The gothic touch seems to echo that of Curwen's friend and fellow Whig, Charles IInd Duke of Norfolk whose hunting lodge by Aira Force, Lyulph's Tower, and, even more, a folly farm immediately outside his castle at Greystoke (mischieveously called Fort Putnam) share the slit windows, castellated skyline, and the massively insistent curtain-wall twenty five feet high. A painting by Alexander Nasmyth around 1810, looking across Windermere from Elleray towards Claife Station emphasises the positive effect that the increased mass brought to the scene. Like Belle Isle itself, the station was only intended for summer use and part of the entertaining effects for visitors was the inclusion of glass of different colours in the windows – blue simulated the cold colour of a winter day, yellow for autumn, green for spring and purple to represent the effect of a threatening storm.

The building had two storeys, the lower part being a dining room and the upper a sitting room. Behind, kitchens and store rooms for supplies were concealed in the massive wall. The building was a tourist amenity, a major and conspicuous object, equipped with a gatehouse by the road and a servant to conduct visitors up the easy curving path that was constructed up the very steep hill.

The Curwens, and their neighbours on Windermere, planted oaks as well as larches and other commercial timber crops on Claife Heights. Such trees now conceal the ruins of this once famous "station", and they certainly obscure that view to the north and south of the length of Windermere. The site is now in the possession of the National Trust (see section 9).

50 Claife Station c.1865
    Detail from photograph
    Francis Frith series no. 3604
    Victoria and Albert Museum

51 Claife Station c.1970
    Photograph Geoffrey Berry

    JOHN DOWNMAN 1750-1824
52 Claife Station 1812
O   From the album:
    A series of sketches on the spot
    made by J. Downman when he took
    a Tour to the Lakes in Westmorland
    and Cumberland 1812
    Victoria and Albert Museum

    THOMAS SUNDERLAND 1744-1823
53 Calgarth New Hall
    Watercolour 36.9 x 50.8 cm.
    Victoria and Albert Museum
The House of Richard Watson, Bishop
of Llandaff (1737-1816) built in 1789-90,
and part of the interlocking social and
aesthetic system developed between
Belle Isle, Storrs and Calgarth in the
middle reaches of Windermere.
Curwen's account book records that in
1798 he planted 'by the desire of my
respected friend Dr. Watson . . . thirty
thousand larches' and a good number of
oaks, to enhance the view across
Windermere from Calgarth.
    Curwen and Watson were both
devoted to the cause of agricultural
reform and improvement. They shared a
characteristically Augustan sense of the
Paradisal bounty of the land, its
benignity which it was the right and
duty of the landowner to increase. In
this aesthetic, the tendency of capital to
grow is a profoundly beautiful
phenomenon.

    J. C. IBBETSON
54 To the Manes of Gilbert
    Wakefield c.1802
    Etching 25.5 x 33.7 cm. (sheet size)
    Published in this series, Harvey and
    Darton London 1817

Victoria and Albert Museum
E4128/41-1902
Ibbetson's comment here makes the
point that even in the high artificiality of
the Arcadian Lake District, and within
the oeuvre of one of its most articulate
celebrants, the real world of dissent
could impinge. Wakefield was a
distinguished classical scholar and
dissenter who died of typhus in 1801
after two years' imprisonment in
Dorchester gaol. He had attacked the
Bishop of Llandaff for absenteeism, and
pointed out furthermore that the
expected French invasion would make
little difference to the oppressed poor of
England. Aesop's ass, he pointed out,
was indifferent when its master exhorted
it to fly with him for the evening:
whoever was master, the ass would
carry the paniers.

5

Ibbetson's etching is a deeply coded
reference to this, explicit only in the
inscription. Satire was a dangerous
business around 1800, especially so in a
close aristocratic society like the Lake
District, and Ibbetson in Ambleside was
completely dependent on gentry
patronage. The iconography of classical
and pastoral imagery, in apparently
innocuous painted landscapes, can often
be pointed and serious external
relevance.

55 Rayrigg, photograph of the south front
David Lyons 1984

Restrictions on building round Windermere meant that new houses were either placed on the site of, or were built around traditional settlements. The original house at Rayrigg had a continuous building history of at least 150 years when John Fleming, Wordsworth's closest friend at Hawkeshead school, moved into it in 1790 on his marriage to Jane Taylor, the daughter of a neighbouring house, Belfield. The core of the house faced firmly away from the lake, seeking shelter rather than prospect. During the alterations to the house in the last quarter of the eighteenth century the south front was added, and the orientation of the house altered towards the view of Belle Isle and the newly planted Claife Heights across the lake.

55

BRATHAY HALL AND JOHN HARDEN

The Brathay estate was bought by George Law, a Jamaica merchant in about the summer of 1784. The house was rebuilt between 1794 and 1796; painted white, and rising out of the shaved lawns, it became the most conspicuous object at the head of Windermere, against the backdrop of Loughrigg. Coleridge wrote in his notebook – 'Mr Law's white Palace – a bitch'.

When Mr. Law died in September 1802 the property was let to John Harden (1772-1847), an Irish amateur of the arts, who has left, in his brilliant drawings and watercolours, the most eloquent record of the cultivated society and consciously Arcadian existence of Windermere in the early nineteenth century. His drawings, of interiors with music parties, of sketching trips and picnics by boat on the lake, make up a wonderful corpus of English Biedermeier imagery.

JOHN HARDEN 1772–1842

56　Brathay Hall 28 August 1808
○　Watercolour body colour on grey
　　paper 14.7 x 22.9 cm.
　　Abbot Hall Art Gallery Kendal

57　On Windermere picnic and sailing
　　Watercolour 14.7 x 21.6 cm.
　　Abbot Hall Art Gallery Kendal

58　Jessy Harden and her sister
　　Catherine Allan at Brathay Hall
　　drawing and reading 1805
　　Pen, ink and wash 13.4 x 19.7 cm.
　　Abbot Hall Art Gallery Kendal

59　View of Windermere with an artist
　　perhaps Harden himself, sketching
　　from a boat 21 September 1805
　　Monochrome wash in a sketchbook
　　page size
　　26.1 x 38.1 cm.
　　Abbot Hall Art Gallery Kendal

60　View of Windermere with an artist
　　perhaps Harden himself, sketching
　　on the shore September 1805
　　Monochrome wash in the same
　　sketchbook as no. 59, page size
　　26.1 x 38.1 cm.
　　Abbot Hall Art Gallery Kendal

61　Clappersgate 31 July 1810
　　15.2 x 24.8 cm.
　　Abbot Hall Art Gallery Kendal

JANE NASMYTH 1788–1866

62　The Langdale Pikes and Brathay
　　Hall from Helm Crag
　　Waterhead 1841
　　Oil on canvas 67.4 x 88.9 cm.
　　The Clonterbrook Trust

DERWENTWATER:
BUILDINGS AND FESTIVALS

In the practical, architectural achievement of an eighteenth century Arcadia in the Lake District, Windermere was supreme, but on Derwentwater the culture flourished, idiosyncracy of personalities contributing the interesting differences. The outstanding personality was Joseph Pocklington, scion of a banking family in Newark, Nottinghamshire, who acquired Vicar's Isle in Derwentwater and began building there in 1778. He was living in the Island House by 1780. In September 1785 he began another house at Portinscale; and in March 1787, yet another, Barrow Cascade House. There were also numerous small buildings, 'follies', boat-houses, stables, the cottage at the Bowder Stone (1789), all forming an elaborate system, partly scenic-architectural, partly recreational. His houses tended to form a part of each other's views.

He was a great entertainer, the patron of festivals such as Keswick Regatta, organized in conjunction with his friend Peter Crosthwaite. The Regattas, culminating in the mock attack on the island, the popular feasting and drinking, under the aegis of local magnates, contributed much to the developing character of Derwentwater and Keswick.

The scholar and antiquarian William Gell in 1797 was 'disgusted with the folly and childishness of what is now called Pocklington's Island,

64

where there is a house that appears to have dropped from the clouds, one or two batteries with pasteboard battlements and a spruceness in the whole, which cannot accord in any degree with the surrounding scenery'.

Gell's fastidious taste was shared with others of the high Picturesque generation of the 1790's, and he himself built a holiday house in Grasmere according to a very different model, whereby the occupant hoped to enjoy his surroundings while impinging as little as possible on the landscape. A similar structure was put up by John Wilson at Elleray on Windermere, but the only survivor of this sort of Picturesque house seems to be Derwent Bay House, also known as Waterend, which belonged to Lord William Gordon. Meanwhile on Ullswater and in the imaginations of designers, other answers to the problem of building suitably in places with a strong existing character were explored.

67

63 Crosthwaite's map of
    Derwentwater (see no. 13)

    J. SMITH
64 Pocklington's Island
    Keswick Lake 1794
    Etching and aquatint, J. Merigot
    hand coloured 33 x 47 cm.
    From the series *Views of the
    Lakes in Cumberland and Westmorland*
    King's College Cambridge Bicknell
    Collection (see no. 40)

    J. M. W. TURNER 1775-1851
65 Derwentwater 1798
    Watercolour
    49.3 x 63 cm.
    Trustees of the British Museum
    Turner Bequest (TB. XXXVI-H)
    One of two worked up versions of p.82
    in the Tweed and Lakes Sketchbook the
    other for presentation to Joseph
    Farington (now lost). Farington was a
    melancholy observer of the changing
    Lake District, and tried to ignore the

new houses. Turner, a lifelong enthusiast for the new, included the main Pocklington sites in his southward view.

JOHN HARDEN
66   Villa at Portinscale
     Watercolour, gouache
     14.1 x 23.5 cm.
     Abbot Hall Art Gallery Kendal
The house in the drawing must be Pocklington's second major Derwentwater house, begun in September 1785.

JOHN BAVERSTOCK KNIGHT
1785-1859
67   Barrow Cascade House
     Watercolour 27.9 x 45.7 cm.
     Victoria and Albert Museum
     E3432 – 1922
Pocklington's third house, begun March 1787.

EDWARD HASSELL d. 1852
68   Barrow Derwentwater
     Watercolour 21.6 x 28.8 cm.
     Victoria and Albert Museum

E. W. JAMES n.d.
69   Derwent Bay House 1798
     Watercolour
     Viscount Rochdale
The drawing is effectively the earliest reference to the house, and probably constitutes evidence for its building date. Its conception can surely not be much earlier, although Lord William Gordon, who built it, was settled in the area through the 1780's. It is a single storied extension towards the lake of an earlier farm house, and each of the three main rooms – clearly intended for entertainment and holiday use – is orientated towards the views, up, across and down the lake. Visually the idiom it adopts is that of the pavilion, the pitched roof of each structural entity having a different level, like a series of marquees. Its discreet, self-effacing presence in the

landscape, hugging the surface of the shore and surrounded by trees, was praised at the expense of Joseph Pocklington's insistent style: 'What his lordship has done or rather forbone to do shows himself to be a man of much taste for the beauties of natural scenery – unlike his neighbour Mr Pocklington...' (*Catherine Mackintosh, 1802*).

70

70   Elleray, the single storey house
     c. 1850 (demolished c. 1855)
     Photograph, anonymous
     St. Anne's School Windermere
The Gordon style was adopted, perhaps on the advice of the painter Alexander Nasmyth, by John Wilson (1785-1854) who had bought the sixty acre Elleray estate in 1806, presumably to be near Wordsworth. Wilson brought Nasmyth with him, according to Mrs. Jessy Harden, to plan the house and to advise him on its situation. Like Gordon's Derwent Bay House, Elleray had a triple orientation, down, across and up the lake. It was similarly pushed right to the edge of its site – here a platform on the Orrest Head slope – and similarly avoided the charge of intrusiveness by being low, and soon covered in climbing plants.

71 'Christopher North's Cottage'
c.1860 Photograph
Francis Frith series no. 3990
Victoria and Albert Museum
The 'Cottage' was the original Elleray, a
traditional small statesman house, to
which Wilson added the sitting room
extension with full length windows in
his first year of ownership in 1806–7.
The gradation of roofs follows the
Picturesque approval of a varied roof
line, and Wilson's residence in the
Cottage exemplifies one major strain of
Picturesque architectural ideology – the
idealization of the life led by cottagers.
The sycamore was made famous in
Wilson's eulogy of it, in one of his Lake
District essays contributed to
Blackwood's Magazine under the
pseudonym Christopher North.

J. B. PAPWORTH 1775–1847
72 Designs for Rural Residences
consisting of a series of designs
for cottages, small villas and
other buildings   London 1818
Plate 12 Cottage Orné designed for
the neighbourhood of the Lakes
Aquatint, hand coloured
trimmed for binding
Brian Mills
Newcastle upon Tyne
Papworth's book consists of designs
adapted to particular kinds of rural
scenery and function. It represents a
response by the architectural profession
to the Picturesque doctrine that
buildings should disrupt the landscape as
little as possible. With other books of the
epoch, such as P. F. Robinson's *Village
Architecture* (1830), it helped to advance
the argument that a building could in
fact do more than hide itself away: it
could be an ornament, one evident and
fitting outgrowth of the history and the
character of the region. Such doctrine
opened the way for historicising styles,
the 'gothic' and Tudor-Renaissance, and
in the Lake District, a Border region, a
resurgence of castellated styles.

THOMAS HARTWELL HORNE
1780–1862
73 The Lakes delineated in forty
three engravings
London 1816, detail of
Ullswater and Lyulph's Tower
Engraving, John Pye after Joseph
Farington, platemark
25.2 x 32.5 cm.
Trustees of Dove Cottage
Lyulph's Tower, by Francis Horne
(1744–89) for Charles Howard, 11th
Duke of Norfolk, belongs to the first
phase of castellated building in the Lake
District. As an exercise in Walpolean
Gothic, it seems an unexpected house
for a great family to erect for leisure
(hunting) purposes, but it does most
interestingly share the triple orientation
of the later single storey houses. A
drawing in the National Library of
Wales, said to be of Uvedale Price's
Aberystwyth house, designed by Nash
before 1798, is close and may derive
from it; but by the date of Nash's work,
triangular gothic summer houses had
many precedents, and Nash was really
working with Price on something much
more novel, and probably similar to the
Gordon, Gell and Wilson houses.

The castellated design and the name of
Lyulph's Tower allude to the legend of
an earlier tower on the site, built by Ulf,
the first Baron Greystoke. The
historicism of the building thus
represents an attempt to build suitably,
as well as ornamentally, in the
landscape.

73

PAINTERS IN ARCADIA

The first group of painters to visit the Lake District as a definite aesthetic entity in its own right were those, around Sir George Beaumont, who came in more or less direct response to the proposition that it was a sort of Northern Arcadia. The vast institutional influence of Farington in the Royal Academy and of Sir George Beaumont among the connoisseurs, would have added greatly to the sense among painters that a visit to the Lake District was a professional obligation. Accordingly the 1780's and 90's saw an almost uninterpreted sequence of visits by major London painters, or by those who hoped, particularly by adopting the evidently important classical subject matter of the Northern Arcadia, to establish a metropolitan reputation.

The following select list is arranged, as nearly as possible in the order of first visiting, as far as extant records permit. The prevailing impression that contemporary residents in Cumbria received, that the countryside was always crowded with painters, would have been reinforced by the presence of those, like Farington and Joseph Wright of Derby who made repeated visits or settled for prolonged periods.

The effect of all this acitivity was to establish more firmly in the general consciousness the idea of the Lake District as classic ground, the cynosure of eyes that were educated to see its special qualities.

74

1783

THOMAS GAINSBOROUGH 1727-88
74 Langdale Pikes
    Pencil and grey wash 26.7 x 42 cm.
    Private Collection

P. J. DE LOUTHERBOURG 1740-1812
75 Landscape in the Lake District 1785
    Oil on canvas 56.5 x 86 cm.
    Leeds City Art Gallery
Tentatively identified as *Ullswater from Water Millock*, RA 1785. Loutherbourg's first exhibits of Lake District subjects, the pair *Skiddaw in Cumberland* and *A Cottage in Patterdale* (Government Art Collection) were at the Royal Academy of 1784, the year following his tour of the Lakes, possibly in company with his friend Gainsborough.

1784

FRANCIS WHEATLEY 1747-1801
76 Coniston
    Watercolour, pen and ink
    28 x 40 cm.
    Whitworth Art Gallery Manchester

77 Windermere, The Ferry 1784
O   Watercolour 61 x 94 cm.
    Victoria and Albert Museum
    P1 – 1948

1786

JOSEPH FARINGTON 1747-1821
78 View of Cockermouth and Skiddaw
    from Sandy Butts
    17 August 1786
    Watercolour, pen and ink

75(a)

(a) A Cottage in Patterdale with horse
     and cart
     Oil on canvas 39 x 47.5 cm.
     Government Art Collection

(b) Skiddaw in Cumberland, a summer
     evening with a stage coach
     Oil on canvas 39 x 58.1 cm.
     Government Art Collection

overall 18.2 x 32.2 cm.
Birmingham Museum and
Art Gallery
On the day that Farington took this view, Francis Towne, a few miles away, was working on a morning and an afternoon view of the Vale of St John, and an evening view of Raven Crag by Thirlmere.

FRANCIS TOWNE
1740?-1816

Towne's Lake District drawings were not always inscribed with times and dates. There appear also to have been at least three major groups or categories: the numbered sequence of forty drawings which was still intact when Oppé saw it in 1915; drawings made on commission or otherwise for separate sale; smaller, usually monochrome ink and wash drawings, often of 'unconventional' topography, such as the western lakes, not represented in the main groups, and evidently parts of a dismembered sketchbook. The following selection is from the first two groups, the main numbered sequence first.

82

79 FRANCIS TOWNE
A View of Ambleside
Lake Windermere 7 August 1786
No. 1
Watercolour 15.9 x 35.2 cm.
Whitworth Art Gallery Manchester

80 A View at Ambleside near Sir
Michael (le) Flemings in the Road
to Keswick No. 3
Watercolour 15.9 x 47.8 cm.
Trustees of the Tate Gallery

81 Loughrigg Ambleside 'morning
light from the right hand' No. 5
Watercolour 15.9 x 23.9 cm.
Fitzwilliam Museum

82 Rydal Water 'taken at the going off
of a storm ... Rydal Water with Mr.
James's and Sir Michael Fleming...'
No. 8 Watercolour 15.7 x 23.7 cm.
Victoria and Albert Museum
P19 – 1921

83 Lake of Windermere looking from
Ambleside No. 10
Watercolour 15.6 x 47.4 cm.
Birmingham Museum and
Art Gallery

84 Part of Ambleside, at the Head of
○ the Lake of Windermere, Morning
Effect 7 August 1786 No. 11
Watercolour 15.7 x 23.8 cm.
Victoria and Albert Museum
P24 – 1924

85 View at the Head of the Lake of
Windermere No. 14
Watercolour 15.6 x 47.4 cm.
Birmingham Museum and
Art Gallery

86 Windermere 'near to Turnpike' 16
August 1786 No. 15
Watercolour 9.6 x 15.5 cm.
Leeds City Art Gallery

87 Elterwater 'light from the left hand'
○ 12 August 1786 No. 19
Watercolour 15.6 x 47.8 cm.
Trustees of Dove Cottage

88 Raven Crag Thirlmere 'light from
the left hand 12 o'clock' 17 August
1786 No. 31
Watercolour 15.6 x 23.7 cm.
Syndics of the Fitzwilliam
Museum Cambridge

89 The Vale of St. John '5 o'clock in the
afternoon light from the left hand'
17 August 1786 No. 36

Watercolour 15.6 x 33.7 cm.
Leeds City Art Gallery

90　On the Lake of Ullswater going
　　down to it from Gobarrow Park
　　No. 37
　　Watercolour 13.5 x 15.5 cm.
　　Leeds City Art Gallery

91　From Rydal Hall Park 'light from
　　the right hand after noon'
　　Watercolour 37.9 x 26.8 cm.
　　Leeds City Art Gallery

This and the following three drawings
seem to be independent of the 'main'
numbered series. They are on sheets of
paper of a different format, and they
seem to have a more considered, less
occasional character. Some of the sheets
in the 'main sequence' date from long
after the 1786 tour, and may have been
worked up to a state of comparable
finish to encourage commissions.
Drawings such as this, on the other
hand, may be the fruits of commissions,
or possibly exhibits in Towne's one-man
show in Lower Brook Street in 1805.

92　A View of Keswick Lake and
　　Skiddaw 1786
　　Watercolour 21.2 x 66.7 cm.
　　Leeds City Art Gallery

93　A View of Keswick Lake looking
　　towards the head
　　Watercolour 20.7 x 22.7 cm.
　　Leeds City Art Gallery

90

94　A View from the Cascade in
　　the Groves at Ambleside
　　10 August 1786
　　Watercolour 37.8 x 26.5 cm.
　　Visitors of the Ashmolean
　　Museum Oxford

In his inscription Towne adds this
memorandum:
　　N.B. The paper this is drawn on I
　　brought myself from Rome!
Towne's visit to the Lake District was
undertaken with two Exeter friends,
James White and John Merivale,
amateur artists who took lessons from
him and were his patrons.

The same relation presumably existed
between John Emes, professional
draughtsman and engraver, and Sir
Robert Cotton, 5th Bart., of
Combermere Abbey in Cheshire. Sir
Robert must the the R.C. Cotton, of
hitherto obscure identity, responsible for
the two drawings in the British
Museum. Emes' hand resembles that of
Thomas Hearne, a stylistic similarity
originating no doubt in their common
apprenticeship to William Woollet, but
Emes, lacking the crucial patronage of
Beaumont, did not reach the Lake
District until 1790. The next year he
showed two views of Derwentwater at
the Royal Academy, one from Fawe
Park and one from Castle Crag, both
now lost. The paired drawings shown
here, with two by Cotton, should date
from the same time.

1790

JOHN EMES fl. 1785–1809
95　Stockghill Force Ambleside
　　Watercolour 48 x 37.8 cm.
　　Trustees of the British Museum
Engraved in aquatint by S. Alken for
Sixteen Views . . . to be bound within
West's Guide.

96　Skelwith Force
　　Watercolour 48 x 37.8 cm.
　　Trustees of the British Museum

101

SIR ROBERT COTTON c. 1735-1807
97a Derwentwater; view from Shansag
Bay to Borrowdale
Pen, indian ink, wash and
watercolour
20.2 x 26.4 cm.
Trustees of the British Museum

97b Derwentwater; view from Shansag
Bay to Stable Hills
Pencil and watercolour
20.2 x 26.1 cm.
Trustees of the British Museum

JOHN LAPORTE c. 1761-1839
98 Album of drawings made on a
tour of 1790
Trustees of the British Museum

99 A Ferry, Keswick Lake
Bodycolour
37.3 x 52.5 cm.
Syndics of the Fitzwilliam
Museum Cambridge

1791

After Towne's visit with James White,
another pupil, and White's nephew, John
White Abbott, made the tour. Like his
master he dated his drawings in a
numbered sequence.

JOHN WHITE ABBOTT 1763-1851
100 Langdale Pikes from Low Wood
12 July 1791 No. 60
Watercolour
24.1 x 18.9 cm.
Victoria and Albert Museum

EDWARD DAYES 1763-1804
101 Windermere
Watercolour 17.2 x 25.4 cm
Victoria and Albert Museum

102 Derwentwater
Watercolour 17.2 x 25.4 cm.
Victoria and Albert Museum

1792

JOSEPH HALFPENNY 1748-1811
103 Bridge House Ambleside
14 July 1792
Watercolour 33 x 51.7 cm.
Victoria and Albert Museum

1793

PAUL SANDBY 1730/1-1809
104 Keswick Lake 1793
Watercolour 36.8 x 54.6 cm.
Aberdeen Art Gallery
One of two drawings at Aberdeen,
unseen before this exhibition which, if
right in location, authorship and date
should establish a visit by Sandby to the
Lake District in 1793 or earlier. Other
Lake District subjects by Sandby include
the undated gouache: Part of Ullswater,
with Dunmallet, in the Clonterbrook
Trust Collection; and the several studies
of Force Bridge and the nearby
waterfalls on the River Kent, five miles
south of Kendal, all at Carlisle Art
Gallery. These last studies resulted in
Sandby's exhibition piece in 1809, the
year of his death: *View of a small Iron
Forge on the River Kent in Cumberland.*

JOSEPH WRIGHT OF DERBY 1734–97
105 Landscape with Boulder
    Watercolour 47 x 56.5 cm.
    Derby Museum and Art Gallery
Wright, a friend of Daniel Daulby, was
presumably in the Lake District
intermittently if not frequently between
1783 and his death in 1797. In this
drawing he seems to be making a
movement towards the 'close-up'
aesthetic of the 1790's.

WILLIAM TATE fl. 1770–1806
106 Portrait of Daniel Daulby
    (1745/6–1798) c.1774
    Oil on canvas 76.5 x 63.5 cm.
    Walker Art Gallery Liverpool
It is too easy to think of the common
culture, especially in a small country, as
London-centred. Daulby, his brother in
law William Roscoe, William Tate and
Joseph Wright of Derby stand
symbolically here for the life and energy
of provincial culture, the equal in
originality of output, in scholarship and
critical appreciation, of anything in
London. Daulby, a martyr to gout,
retired slowly from business in
Liverpool, renting Rydal Mount on and
off from 1783 until he leased it formally
on his retirement in 1796, the year in
which he published a pioneering work in
English on Rembrandt. Like the
Curwen-Watson set on Windermere, he
was an enthusiast for agricultural
improvement. His wife and daughters
took to dairying in fulfilment of the
Arcadian dream. He wrote to Roscoe, 4
August 1796: 'Margaret enters into the
true spirit of farming . . . she makes her
fifth cheese tonight from the two cows
which have given seven pounds of
Butter fat . . .'.

1796

ABRAHAM PETHER 1756–1812
107 Thirlmere
    Oil on canvas 61.4 x 92 cm.
    Manchester City Art Gallery
A date of 1801 is tentatively suggested,
perhaps linking the picture with Pether's
exhibit at the Academy that year
Moonlight – view from Nature (no. 13). In
1796 he had shown *A View in
Cumberland* (no. 39), the only named
Lake District subject in his exhibited
oeuvre.

105

Detail of 108

1797
J.M.W. TURNER
1775-1851

Exhibited at the Royal Academy 1798 (no. 196) with the lines slightly adapted from the Morning Hymn in Milton's Paradise Lost (Book V) in which Adam and Eve call upon the elements of the natural world to praise the creator:

> Ye mists and exhalations that now rise
> From hill or streaming [sic] lake, dusky or grey,
> Till the sun paints your fleecy skirts with gold,
> In honour to the world's great author, rise!

Turner's response to the Arcadian/paradisal ideal of the Lake District was mythic as well as immediately sensuous. In the central sward of the picture a man and woman stand with their sheep grazing before them, the sole human figures in the vast landscape, who precisely but unemphatically identify the Lake District paradise with that of Adam and Eve. The pciture divides almost equally, the lower half is concerned with descent into the dark; while the upper has lines of hills stretching into a less definite, more ethereal, region of light and infinity.

At the very moment that Turner was using the passage of Milton to make this statement about a possible paradise in the Lakeland hills, Wordsworth was in Germany struggling to articulate and so recover his own paradisal memories of schooldays at Hawkshead. Wordsworth's first drafts of the poem that became *The Prelude*, show him using the Morning Hymn as a rhetorical structure; his phrases are religious in mood, secular in phrasing, but, like Milton and Turner he was addressing the forces that make up a paradise in which the human being can live:

> Ye presence of Nature, in the sky
> And on the earth! Ye visions of the hills!
> And Souls of lonely places!

Wordsworth's first book of *The Prelude*, in its earliest versions, is an affirmation of belief through a dark, negative questioning: "Was it for this...?" – his temporary failure to achieve anything as a poet – that the River Derwent, the mountains, the lakes and the winds had taken such loving, if strange, care of him as a child. In Turner's painting, the implicit dualism is less personal, and more absolute: it is in the dark fall that flows in the contrary and downward direction, away from the paradise aloft.

J. M. W. Turner

108 Morning amongst the Coniston
○ Fells 1798
      Oil on canvas 123 x 89.7 cm.
      Turner Bequest by courtesy of the
      Trustees of the Tate Gallery

109 Buttermere Lake with Part of
○ Cromackwater, Cumberland
      a Shower 1798
      Oil on canvas 91.5 x 122 cm.
      Turner Bequest by courtesy of the
      Trustees of the Tate Gallery
Exhibited at the RA 1798 (no. 527) with
lines adapted from Thompson's *Spring*
(11.189-205). The significance of Spring
(as Prosperina annually returns from
Hades) is redemptive, and in Turner's
picture is given its Judaic symbol of the
rainbow. The two Lake District pictures
of 1798 are thus pendants of one another,
playing on the Arcadian-Paradisal theme
with ideas of fragility, transience, and
triumphant returning.

110 Sketchbook for 1797 bound in calf
      with seven brass clasps
      Eighty-nine leaves 37.1 x 26.6 cm.
      Watermarked 1794 and 1796
      Turner Bequest TB XXXV, by
      courtesy of the Trustees of the
      British Museum
Open at p. 57, inscribed 'Old Man' (of
Coniston), the sketch containing the
idea for the upper part of *Morning
amongst the Coniston Fells*

111 Ullswater with Patterdale
      old Hall 1797
      Watercolour 25.8 x 37.1 cm.
      Syndics of the Fitzwilliam Museum
A sheet cognate with no. 65, possibly
also from the group now known as TB
XXXVI, and substantiating Turner's
interest in the evidences of human
presence in the landscape, both past and
present. The human significance of the
Old Hall for Turner would have been
sharpened by articles in the *Gentleman's
Magazine* about the 'Queen of

Patterdale', the pipe smoking wife of
Mr. Mounsey, the lord of the manor,
alias the 'King'.

112 Ambleside Mill Westmorland
      Watercolour 36.8 x 25.4 cm.
      University of Liverpool
A finished watercolour, like (no. 111),
derived from p. 51 of the Tweed and
Lakes sketchbook. 'Industrial' subjects,
like the *Ambleside Mill* and the Slate
Wharf subjects, were deeply a part of the
pictorial tradition by the turn of the
century, showing how the earth with its
riches of materials and energy serves the
legitimate interests of mankind.

113 Ullswater Lake from
      Gowbarrow Park
      Watercolour
      28 x 41.3 cm.
      Whitworth Art Gallery Manchester
A drawing made c. 1818 for Turner's
important Yorkshire patron, Walter
Fawkes of Farnley Hall, for which he
reworked material from the Tweed and
Lakes book, and used the old
amphitheatrical compositional idiom,
which had otherwise virtually
disappeared from his repertoire.

114 Coniston Water with Tent
      Lodge c. 1818
      Watercolour and gouache on grey
      paper 50.1 x 66 cm.
      Syndics of the Fitzwilliam Museum
Another drawing for Walter Fawkes, but
in the 'progressive', chromatically bold
style, more characteristic of the Fawkes
collection. The subject, Tent Lodge,
demonstrates Turner's lively interest in
the contemporary development of the
Lake District. Tent Lodge was built
1806-7 by George Smith as a memorial
to his remarkable daughter Elizabeth
(1776-1806), poet, scholar, linguist and
fell-walker, who died of consumption
having spent the last year of her life
within sight of Coniston, in a tent
erected for her occasional use.

115 Winander Mere Westmorland
  Watercolour and gouache
  29 x 46 cm.
  City Art Gallery Manchester
A drawing made for the *England and Wales* series of engraved views (this subject engraved by J. T. Willmore, 1837), Turner's summation in late middle age of the topographical riches of the kingdom. The *Windermere* is a celebration of precisely that atmosphere of waterborne festival built up by the early villa residents, and which reached its climax at the Regatta of August 1825. Turner would not have witnessed such a scene on his Lake District trip of 1797, but he could have heard of it from Walter Scott, or even, given the date of the engraving, picked up the vivid account in Lockhart's *Memoirs of the Life of Sir Walter Scott*, published 1836-8.

1798

  J. C. IBBETSON 1759-1817
116 Ullswater from Gowbarrow 1801
  Oil on canvas 147.2 x 209.5 cm.
  Leeds City Art Gallery
It was Daulby's brother in law William Roscoe who in 1798 suggested to Ibbetson that he come to Rydal. Daulby was dead and his wife had returned from her short pastoral idyll to Liverpool. Ibbetson, a restless and socially unassimilated personality, settled himself in Clappersgate and began producing some of the most eloquent images of self conscious pastoralism achieved by any artist. Both Daulby and Roscoe were passionate anti-slavers as well as idealists about liberal capitalism. Ibbetson's views, evident in his Gilbert Wakefield etching seem to have been similar.

117 The Painter's House
  Ambleside 1803
  Oil on panel 30.5 x 41.6 cm.
  Ferens Art Gallery
  Kingston upon Hull

118 Windermere from Troutbeck 1803
  Oil on canvas 58.4 x 76.2 cm.
  Ferens Art Gallery
  Kingston upon Hull

1800

117

THOMAS GIRTIN 1775-1802
119 The Gorge of Watendlath with
  the Falls of Lodore
  Derwentwater Cumberland
  Watercolour
  53.5 x 44.6 cm.
  Visitors of the Ashmolean
  Museum Oxford
Girtin's visit to the Lake District is putative, based on the uncertain topography of this wonderful drawing. On stylistic grounds the drawing is dated to 1801.

  It was bought directly from the artist by Edward Lascelles (1764-1814) who also bought heavily from Turner – his name being recorded for two Harewood Castle views and a Kirkstall Abbey in the covers of TB XXXIV, used by Turner for the earlier part of his 1797 tour. In elaboration and monumentality the Girtin rivals the finished Turner drawings of 1798.

119

PAUL SANDBY MUNN 1773–1845
120 Lower End of Rydal Water 1810
    Watercolour 38.7 x 61.6 cm.
    Towneley Hall Burnley
A drawing of cottages at Portinscale in
the Victoria and Albert Museum locates
Munn's first visit to the Lakes in 1800;
further fine graphite studies of cottages
in the Picturesque idiom are dated
August 1804, and a further group 1809.
The tour of the latter year presumably
gave rise to this finished Rydal subject.

1802

JOHN CROME 1768–1821
121 Slate Quarries c.1802–5
    Oil on canvas 123.9 x 158.6 cm.
    Trustees of the Tate Gallery
The topography of this landscape is
obviously doubtful, and the picture
probably represents a general memory
of quarrying in various locations, from
the Lake District and Wales to
Mousehold Heath. Crome was however
in the Lake District in 1802. Entries in
the diary of Hannah Gurney (in the
possession of a descendant) record his
presence with the Gurney party at
Keswick on 14 August. He goes
sketching with the girls, whose drawing
master he was, and he leaves for
Norwich on 28 August. His next
recorded trip, again with the Gurneys,
was in 1806: the visits thus neatly
bracket the conventional stylistic dating
for the *Slate Quarries*.

ANTHONY V. C. FIELDING 1787–1855
122 Rydal Mountains 1806
    Watercolour 20.7 x 31.4 cm.
    Victoria and Albert Museum
From 1802, Fielding's family lived at
Ambleside and Keswick, and the Lake
District was thus fundamental to his
sense of landscape at the outset of his
long career.

1803

WILLIAM GREEN 1761–1823
123 Wastwater: view from
    Latterbarrow 1807
    Pencil 48.2 x 67 cm.
    Victoria and Albert Museum
Green came into the Lake District first as
a surveyor from Manchester in 1778,
and was induced to become an artist by
Thomas West, whose *Guide* at the same
time vastly increased the market for
views of the Lakes.

By the early 1790's Green was an
independent artist, visiting the Lakes
and publishing prints. In 1800 he settled
at Ambleside and opened shops both
there and at Keswick. He and Ibbetson
are the outstanding examples of
northern opportunism and
entrepreneurial energy in developing the
pictorial identity of the Lake District,
Green being especially important as a
cicerone for draughtsmen such as Glover
and Hills who came after him and drew
on his local knowledge. Hills (see no.
137) for example would have been
hardly likely to penetrate to Wastwater
in 1803 without Green's advice.

Green's manuscript journals and his
Tourist Guide (1819) are an invaluable
source of knowledge of the comings and
goings of artists in the period.

124 The Tourist's New Guide
    2 volumes Kendal 1819
    12 or 24 aquatints in printer's
    colours
    Trustees of Dove Cottage
This was the most complete guide to the

49

19

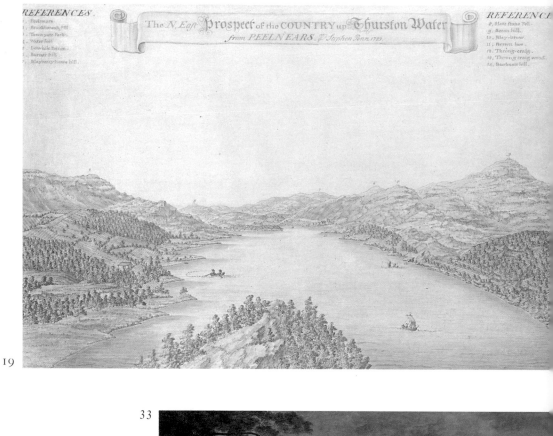

33

34

41

42

43

47

48

77

84

87

127

129

137

140

151

154

159

161

188

lakes, covering those areas, especially the remoter valleys of the south west such as Wastwater omitted from the earlier books.

125 Sixty coloured aquatints described
in the *New Guide*
published separately
Ambleside 1815 – open at
Scandale Beck
King's College Cambridge
Bicknell Collection

Green's contact with Hills evidently put him in touch with the 'close up' studies pursued in the early years of the century by the London watercolourists.

126 Forty Etchings from Nature: of Old
Buildings situate in the
Mountainous District of the North
of England
Ambleside 1822
40 soft ground etchings
King's College Cambridge
Bicknell Collection

These were the first forty of a proposed series of two hundred 'Scenes of Farm Houses, Cottages, Abbies, Churches, Castles, Old Halls, and Bridges', which was never completed. Green's enormous output of drawings and prints of Lake District buildings, observed with the eye of a professional surveyor, constitutes not only a major achievement of Picturesque graphic art, but an important architectural record, comparable in both respects with the nearly contemporary work of J. S. Cotman.

JOHN GLOVER 1767-1849
127 Ullswater with Goldrigg Bridge
O Oil on canvas 90 x 131 cm.
Government Art Collection, by
courtesy of the Secretary of State
for Agriculture

128 Borrowdale
Watercolour 41.9 x 61 cm.
Laing Art Gallery

Newcastle on Tyne

John Glover worked at Appleby Grammar School, Leicestershire, as a writing master from 1786-1793. He had visited the Lakes by 1795 for in that year he exhibited his first painting at the Royal Academy, View of Ryddol, Cumberland. His visit in company with Robert Hills in 1803, when they both had the advantage of William Green acting as their guide and fellow artist, was the beginning of a new metropolitan interest in the Lake District (partly a consequence of the renewed war with France). Glover especially helped to feed into the early exhibitions of the Society of Painters in Watercolours, founded in 1805, a rich representation of Lake District landscape. In 1805 there was only one image from the Lake District and that was by Glover; in 1806 there were sixteen and nine were by Glover; Farington noted Glover's "Great Success ... in selling his drawings of the Lakes", and that Reinagle and Havell in emulation were to go to Westmorland "to store themselves with subjects for drawings". Nor were they alone, for Constable and Joseph Powell were two others who had reached the Lake District by the end of the year. In 1807 Glover had eleven pieces dedicated to Lake District subjects, and subsequently about one third of his exhibited output exploited this vein.

Glover had a clear sense of his art as belonging in the same descent as that of Richard Wilson, and of the supreme authority in landscape of the Claudian tradition. Glover's image of the lakes was emphatically Arcadian. His preferred subjects were of the area about Ullswater, on the banks of which he had a farm. This he sold about 1820 in order to buy a painting by Claude; it was then his custom to exhibit his own work with that of Claude (and a Poussin and a Richard Wilson), for the purpose of comparison.

Hills, like Glover, a founder member and office holder of the Society of
Painters in Watercolours, similarly mounted a public discourse of
Arcadianism in his exhibited landscapes, including those that derived
from his seminal 1803 journey to the Lakes. Yet the drawings from that
tour bear in a sense on a very different aesthetic, and are the precise
equivalent of the work done in the same year by Joshua Cristall and
Cornelius Varley in Wales. The intellectual background against which
they were all working was that of the Pricean Picturesque, which
rationalized the change in the focus of aesthetic activity from the prospect
and the panorama to the close-up, the infinitely varied and 'naturally
composed' effects of Nature as encountered by the wayside. To this, the
brilliant circle around Cornelius Varley – surely the genius of the group –
added the insights provided by Varley's work on optics at the outset of
his career as a designer of optical scientific apparatus. Drawings by
people associated with him thus tend to re-enact the way that the eye, or
any lens, works most sharply through its centre, producing a central area
of particular focus and throwing those parts of the field of vision that are
not subject to this distinguishing effect into indistinctness. The effect
works both in close-up, as in the Wastwater boulder drawing (see no.

130

137) and for the distance, where the technique tends to reverse the
academic doctrine of aerial perspective whereby the darker foreground
graduates to a paler and less sharply apprehended distance: in Hills'
vision, the foreground may be part of the periphery, barely traced over
white paper, and the distance brightly – even darkly – coloured, as the
eye drives through the intervening air like a telescope to its point of
interest (Derwentwater from Sprinkling Tarn, no. 133).

The wider group – Hills, Cristall, Havell, the minor figures James
Holworthy and Joseph Powell, and the much greater figure of John

Constable – show also in drawings here (Hills' *Slate Quarry*, no. 134; Cristall's *Fall in Borrowdale*, no. 140): – the development of an esoteric cult of the sketch). In these years and through most of the nineteenth century, artists and connoisseurs held that the sketch, with its brilliant rapidity of execution and its gestural testimony to a moment of creative energy in front of the subject, had a prime status as a work of art, prior to and therefore more 'authentic' than the finished picture.

In these developments the approaching end of the domination in visual art of the Arcadian-classical aesthetic is evident. The exhibitions, mediating the major public statements of artists, remained showcases of institutionalised classicism. Artists such as Constable, determined to achieve sonority and monumentality in landscape art, struggled with the compositional language and the limits of inclusiveness in classic art, towards the achievement of an authentic classic utterance for his times. But privately, and more widely in the culture, the expression of idealism about the landscape, about its significance for human good, ceased to find expression in a pictorial tradition concerned with discovering the evidences of Arcadia in the native scene.

131

ROBERT HILLS

129 Skelwith Force
   ○ Watercolour over pencil
      37.1 x 26.7 cm.
      Birmingham City Museum and
      Art Gallery

130 Cottages at Nab Scar
    Pencil and wash 20 x 29.7 cm.
    Birmingham City Museum and
    Art Gallery

131 Pavy Ark, one of the Pikes of
    Langdale; a cheese press
    Watercolour over pencil
    24.3 x 29.4 cm.
    Birmingham City Museum and
    Art Gallery

132 Vale of Newlands near Buttermere
    Pencil
    23.3 x 28.6 cm.
    Birmingham City Museum and
    Art Gallery

133 Derwentwater from Sprinkling
    Tarn (The peaks numbered and
    titled at the right)
    Watercolour over pencil
    23.7 x 28.8 cm.
    Birmingham City Museum and
    Art Gallery

134 Slate Quarry Langdale
    Watercolour over pencil
    37.3 x 26.5 cm.
    Birmingham City Museum and
    Art Gallery

135 Roadside Borrowdale, looking
    towards the Bowder Stone
    Watercolour and pencil
    Trustees of the British Museum
    1876-12-9-1076

136 Near Clappersgate
    Watercolour
    Trustees of the British Museum
    1876-12-9-1050

137 Wastwater, a boulder with moss
o Watercolour
   Trustees of the British Museum
   1876-12-9-1051

138 Grange in Borrowdale
   Watercolour
   Trustees of the British Museum
   1876-12-9-1066

139 Lake of Wyburn, Saddleback in
   the distance
   Watercolour
   Trustees of the British Museum
   1876-12-9-1072

1805

   JOSHUA CRISTALL 1768-1847
140 A Fall in Borrowdale
 o Watercolour
    29.1 x 20.3 cm.

Victoria and Albert Museum
E1893-1920

141 A scene near the Bowder Stone
   Borrowdale Cumberland
   Watercolour 27.4 x 40.3 cm.
   Victoria and Albert Museum FA22
A simple contrast between Cristall in his
esoteric mode, carrying the experience
of companionship with Cornelius Varley
in Wales two years before into the the
Lake District in 1805, and his public-
professional mode of classicizing
utterance for the Watercolour Society of
1814. Albums of drawings by Cristall
for his tour of July 1805 are in the British
Museum, 1876-12-9-923. They
exquisitely fulfil the promise of the 1803
Welsh tour, and are a crucial record of
the minute, detailed vision cultivated
within the Varley circle during these
years.

JAMES HOLWORTHY 1781-1841
142 Sketchbook c.1805 open at
pp.70-71:
'Lower End of Ullswater at Pooly'
'Ullswater Lower End'
Watercolour page size
27 x 36.5 cm.
Victoria and Albert Museum
Holworthy, a founder member of the
Society of Painters in Watercolours, has
been virtually lost to history, subsumed
into the reputation of Glover. Another
sketchbook in the Victoria and Albert
Museum, dated 1805, in which his name
is inscribed, partially explains this
through the close similarity of style in
such aspects as the 'split-brush'
technique of wash drawing. Glover is
said to have been Holworthy's teacher,
and he perhaps made free with his
pupil's book: another page bears a
graphite study of the bridge at
Buttermere, the subject of Glover's
watercolour in the Victoria and Albert
Museum (P148-1931). It could suggest

some deep collaboration. Yet these
sheets shown here, and others in the two
books, are evidence of an original and
major talent, and of full participation in
the 'sketch aesthetic' of his institutional
peers. The splashing of the sheets with
water and certain inscriptions earlier in
the book referring to 'light covering of
watery cloud' prompt comparison with
Constable's watercolour sketches in the
Lake District.

FRANCIS NICHOLSON 1753-1844
143 Lake Windermere
Watercolour 38 5 x 53 5 cm.
Whitworth Art Gallery Manchester
A visit to the Lakes in 1805 is indicated
by the appearance of a Windermere and
a Hawes Water view at the Society of
Painters in Watercolours the next year.
Nicholson was slightly before the main
rush of young painters in 1806-7, and
interestingly, as a member of an older
generation, he takes no part in the cult of
the sketch among the young.

143

Constable came to the Lake District in 1806 at the suggestion of his uncle David Pike Watts (1754–1816), a deeply pious man, conscious that painting could be a vocation and concerned that his nephew's career should develop with a proper knowledge of the springs of landscape art at its finest and most serious. Watts had demonstrated his admiration for the special qualities of Lake District scenery by acquiring in 1804 Storrs Hall on Windermere (see no. 46).

Thither Constable went, staying there and at Brathay Hall (no. 56) with the Hardens until about the middle of September when he moved on to Borrowdale, completing in the whole period before his return to London late October some seventy-seven (at least) graphite and wash drawings, and perhaps some landscape work in oil. This major efflorescence of activity, topographically at odds with his characteristic subject matter, has been often misinterpreted as foreshadowing in some way his later interests in clouds and other 'meteorological' effects. Certainly it is right to see his drawings in close relation as here to those of his contemporaries – London professionals who visited the Lakes and many of the same houses in the years immediately before he did; yet Constable's main experimental interest in these drawings tends to be compositional, as he studies the large structures and relations of objects in the landscape, and their potency of mood and meaning as constituents of an unmistakably classical art. Inscriptions on the drawings themselves show that his frame of reference was to Claude and Gaspard Poussin, and there is little doubt that Constable here, as throughout his career, was primarily concerned with the landscape as the vehicle of a noble and elevated discourse in the tradition to which he felt his work must belong.

1806

JOHN CONSTABLE
1776–1837

John Constable

144 Langdale Pikes from above
   Skelwith Fold 4 Sept 1806
   Pencil 24.2 x 38.1 cm.
   Spink and Son

If the date is correctly read as
4 September, it suggests that Constable
began exploring towards the Langdale
valley during his stay at Storrs Hall. He
went to Brathay a few days later,
possibly Sunday 7 September, and
certainly found that a more convenient
base for outings towards Skelwith
and Ambleside.

147 Towards Glaramara from
   Watendlath Path
   '25 Sept 1806 – Borrowdale – a fine
   clouday day tone very mellow like –
   the mildest of Gaspar Poussin and
   Sir G(eorge) B(eaumont) and on the
   whole deeper toned than this
   drawing –'
   Watercolour 24.3 x 34.6 cm.
   Victoria and Albert Museum R.74

148 Gate Crag Borrowdale
   Watercolour 44.4 x 34.4 cm.
   Victoria and Albert Museum R.87

145

145 'Saddleback and part of Skiddaw
   Sept 21 – 1806 Stormy day – Noon'
   Watercolour 76 x 29.5 cm.
   Victoria and Albert Museum R.72

146 'Helvellin 21 Sept 1806 – rain
   (deleted) evening – stormy with
   slight rain'
   Watercolour 15.8 x 36.6 cm.
   Victoria and Albert Museum R.73

Constable's drawings, like Francis
Towne's, are often grouped to cover the
times of day, usually morning, noon,
and evening. This arangement
prompted by interest in the
changeability of mood and effect, has
origins in the seventeenth century
landscape tradition, and more
immediate precedent in Loutherbourg's
revolution in stage design in the last
quarter of the eighteenth century, and in
the various visual entertainments that
followed from his Eidophusikon
of 1781.

149 View from the Borrowdale narrows
   towards Glaramara
   Watercolour 34.2 x 44.1 cm.
   Victoria and Albert Museum R.88

150 Glaramara, Gt. End and Gt. Gable
   looking to Sty Head Pass from
   near Rosthwaite
   Watercolour 19.1 x 27.4 cm.
   Victoria and Albert Museum R.89

151 Borrowdale from near Stonethwaite
 o looking south west to Glaramara,
   Stonethwaite Fell and the Sty Head
   Pass
   Pencil 33 x 47 cm.
   Leeds City Art Gallery

152 Upper Borrowdale with Gt. Gable
   in the distance
   'Borrowdale 2 Sept (sic)
   1806 morning previous to a fine day'
   Watercolour 18.1 x 48 cm.
   Victoria and Albert Museum R.76

153 Gt. Gable, Kirk Fell and Pillar
'from the top of Onister Craig Oct 2
1806 – noon'
Watercolour
14.4 x 48.9 cm.
Victoria and Albert Museum R.77

154 A Bridge near Rosthwaite – 'Oct 2
O 1806 – twylight after a very fine day'
Watercolour
18.9 x 27.1 cm.
Victoria and Albert Museum R.78
Nos. 152-4 constitute a trio, morning
noon and evening, culminating in an
explicitly Arcadian scene of the
milkmaid like figure returning with her
pitcher in the evening.

155 Looking into Borrowdale narrows
from the south 'Borrowdale 4 Oct
1806 – Dark Autumnal day at noon
– tone more blooming (than) this . . .
the effect exceeding terrific – and
much like the beautiful Gaspar I saw
in Margaret St.'
Watercolour
19.1 x 27.4 cm.
Victoria and Albert Museum R.80

156 Borrowdale from Rosthwaite
looking north Castle Crag on the
left 'Borrowdale 4 Oct 1806 Noon
Clouds breaking away after Rain'
Watercolour 13.9 x 37.5 cm.
Victoria and Albert Museum R.79
Nos. 155-6 are two drawings for noon
on the same day showing the changing
effects brought about by cloud.

157 'Sty Head Tearn – Borrowdale –
Sunday 12 Oct 1806 – Noon Great
End – Scorfell – Longmell –'
Watercolour 12.1 x 26.9 cm.
Victoria and Albert Museum R.83
The culminating tableau of a group for
12 October composed high up in the
hills around Esk Hause, recorded by
Constable in an inscription on one of the
drawings as 'the finest scenery that ever
was'.

158 Bow Fell, Crinkle Crags and the
Band '19 Oct 1806 Langdale'
Pencil and grey wash
34.4 x 48.6 cm.
Victoria and Albert Museum R.86
A final outing, after his return to
Brathay from Borrowdale, produced
this noble image. The contrast in the
power of rhetoric with the first views of
Langdale (see no. 144) is striking.

JOSEPH POWELL c. 1780-1834
159 Borrowdale 1806
O Watercolour 21.9 x 21.1 cm.
Jonathan Wordsworth
Powell was a profuse exhibitor at the
Academy between 1796 and 1833. His
oeuvre has largely disappeared from
view, but a group of his drawings sold
recently in London show him to have
been closely in touch with other painters
of his generation, with the same duality
between private and public work,
especially in the response, as here, to the
classic landscape of the Lake District.

1807

RAMSAY RICHARD REINAGLE
c. 1775-1862
160 Loughrigg Mountain and the River
Brathay – Sunset 1808
Watercolour 51.1 x 71.1 cm.
Trustees of the Tate Gallery

165

161 Slatewharf at Brathay
 o Watercolour 51.2 x 71 cm.
   Laing Art Gallery
   Newcastle upon Tyne
The image celebrates the sense of the
earth's abundance, in the harvest of its
mineral and agricultural resources.

162 Rydal Mountains, Stormy Day
    Oil on millboard 20 x 26.7 cm.
    Victoria and Albert Museum
    1409-69
Reinagle's visits to the Lake District are
problematical, but it would be logical to
suppose that he was, like his friend and
companion in 1807 William Havell,
already making oil sketches on paper
and board at this time or very soon after.
The same duality between the perfected
Arcadianism of the exhibited works and
the rapid virtuosity of the private would
seem to have existed in his oeuvre as in
that of others of his group.
   This panel was originally one of four
sold by Reinagle for five guineas when
he fell on hard times after his expulsion
from the Royal Academy for plagiarism
in 1849.

   WILLIAM HAVELL 1782-1857
163 Skelwith Force 1807
    Oil on paper 54.2 x 72.6 cm.
    Reading Museum and Art Gallery

164 Keswick Lake 1810
    Watercolour
    53.3 x 71.1 cm.
    Laing Art Gallery
    Newcastle upon Tyne

165 Windermere 1811
    Watercolour 24.8 x 34 cm.
    Trustees of the British Museum
    The date reads either 1811 or
    perhaps 1814.

166 Wetherlam from Little Langdale
    Gouache 35.5 x 50.9 cm.
    Reading Museum and Art Gallery

167 Bracken Cutting near
    Keswick 1835
    Oil on canvas 63.8 x 76.7 cm.
    Reading Museum and Art Gallery

c.1810-30

   EDWARD SWINBURNE 1788-1844
168 Coniston Beck
    Watercolour 34.3 x 30.5 cm.
    Whitworth Art Gallery
    University of Manchester
Identified tentatively as the uncle
of the poet and scion of the great
Northumbrian family, Swinburne seems
to have owed much to Francis
Nicholson.

WILLIAM TURNER of Oxford
1789-1862
169 View from above the Fall at Lodore
Watercolour 61 x 75.5 cm.
Birmingham Museum and
Art Gallery

William Turner first visited the Lakes in 1815, but his main contribution to the visual culture of the area was his series of highly finished exhibition watercolours of the 1840's and later, closely analogous to the work of the Richardsons and Rowbothams in Italianising the scene, and assimilating it to contemporary experience of the north Italian Lakes.

WILLIAM WESTALL 1781-1850
170 Views of the Lake and Vale of
Keswick
London 1820
Trustees of Dove Cottage

12 coloured aquatints, drawn and engraved by Westall; published originally in three parts as the beginning of *Views of the Lakes of Cumberland*.

Westall, from his first visit to the Lakes in 1811, was deeply involved with its society, with Wordsworth and Southey, and he was connected by marriage to Adam Sedgwick, the geologist, an important figure in the religious and intellectual life of the Lake District in the second quarter of the century. The two coloured aquatints shown here especially attracted the favour of Sara Hutchinson, who wrote of *Keswick from the East Side*: 'I could not have believed that an Engraving could have given the quiet and solemn feeling inspired by such a scene' (letter to John Monkhouse, 15 October 1820.) The panorama, *Rydal and Loughrigg*, viewed from the part of the Rydal Mount garden known as Dora's Field was prepared with the co-operation, in topographical expertise, of Wordsworth himself. Westall wrote, 21 October 1831 – 'I am just going to begin the plate of Rydal, I will send a proof, for you to get me the names of the mountains...'

171 Windermere c.1834
Watercolour and gouache
12.7 x 17.4 cm.
Whitworth Art Gallery
University of Manchester

Designed by Westall for Charles Tilt's speculative Landscape Illustrations of the Waverley Novels, with Descriptions of the Views (London 1834), to illustrate *Guy Mannering*, in which the heroine stays for a short time on Windermere and comments on its romantic Paradisal quality.

170

PETER DE WINT
1784-1849

De Wint began exhibiting Lake District subjects in 1821, and he was evidently thereafter a regular visitor especially receiving patronage from the Lonsdales at Lowther and the Howards at Levens Hall. In his work the distinction between the sketch alla prima and the formal exhibited picture continues to be valid, despite the fact that de Wint's modern reputation, founded on the criticism of the late nineteenth century art historians, is concentrated on his sketches. The careful structural technique, the fundamental and abiding commitment to the formal discipline of art, emerges in the juxtaposition of the watercolour *Derwentwater* with the small oil study of foreground weeds (nos. 172-3): even the technical reversal, the oil contributing to the finished watercolour, emphasises the gravitas of de Wint's intentions.

De Wint was deeply pious, seized like his acquaintance John Clare with a profound sense of the beauty and bounty of the world, as in his images of haymaking in the flat lands. This was equally part of his response to the mountains, filled in his panoramic images of their summits with the Christian sense of immanence.

176

PETER DE WINT
172 Derwentwater
Watercolour 59.7 x 99.1 cm.
Lady Lever Art Gallery
Port Sunlight

173 Study of Burdock and other plants
Oil
Trustees of the Tate Gallery

174 Westmorland Hills from Matterdale
Watercolour 15.3 x 64.7 cm.
Whitworth Art Gallery
University of Manchester

175 Bowder Stone Borrowdale
Watercolour
30.1 x 42.7 cm.
Leeds City Art Gallery

176 Trees at Lowther
Watercolour
90.2 x 66.1 cm.
Usher Art Gallery Lincoln

177 Lowther 1839
Watercolour
60.3 x 44.7 cm.
Usher Art Gallery Lincoln

1830-50

EDWARD LEAR 1812-88
178 Windermere from the road from
O Kendal to Bowness 10 July 1836
Watercolour 27.3 x 35.9 cm.
The Clonterbrook Trust

182

179 Helvellyn 15 October 1836
    Black chalk
    17.1 x 25.4 cm.
    The Clonterbrook Trust
Like de Wint, Lear received the
patronage of the Howards at Levens
Hall. He evidently spent the latter part
of the summer and autumn of 1836 in
the Lake District, and wrote to his
publisher, 21 October 1836 –

> 'it is impossible to tell you how, &
> how enormously I have enjoyed the
> whole Autumn. The counties of
> Cumberland and Westmoreland are
> superb indeed, & tho the weather
> has been miserable, yet I have
> contrived to walk pretty well over
> the whole ground, & to sketch a
> good deal besides.'

    J. B. PYNE 1800–70
180 The Druidical Circle Keswick
    Watercolour 29.5 x 47 cm.
    Manchester City Art Gallery
Pyne's experience of the Lake District
dates from c.1834, but his major
achievement, the drawings and
paintings associated with the great series
of lithographs *The English Lake District*
dates from 1848.
    The 'Druidical Circle', a frequent

subject of Lake District painters, is
included here to show how fundamental
a part of the Arcadian view of the Lakes
was the sense of a pre-history – a golden
age lost in the mists of antiquity. The
druidic myth, associated with the
Keswick stone circle, thus served
something of the purpose locally of the
Graeco-Roman monuments in the
Mediterranean.

181 Thirlmere
    Watercolour 33.7 x 48.7 cm.
    Birmingham Museum and
    Art Gallery
The watercolour version of the subject
lithographed by W. Gauci for *The English
Lake District* (London, Agnew, 1853). A
version in oils is in the Sunderland Art
Gallery.

    ALFRED VICKERS 1786–1868
182 Thirlmere
    Oil on canvas 18.1 x 26 cm.
    Manchester City Art Gallery
Vickers was a ubiquitous tourist, but his
first named Lake District subject at the
Academy did not appear until 1844 (no.
236, *Rydal Water*). In 1859 his second and
last appeared, *The Lake of Thirlmere, foot
of Helvellyn, Cumberland* (no. 550).

HOME AT GRASMERE

The Grasmere that Wordsworth and his sister came to as tenants of Dove Cottage in 1799 was still physically as Thomas Gray had come upon it in 1769 – 'this little unsuspected paradise (where) all is peace, rusticity, and happy poverty, in its neatest and most becoming attire'. There were fine houses that had to be 'juggled away' by Dorothy Wordsworth from her views, for the first Arcadian phase of Lake District development had reached Rydal, and in Grasmere Allan Bank was a conspicuous object under Helm Crag (see Ibbetson, 1801, no. 186). Wordsworth described in the poem, 'Home at Grasmere' how the Vale appeared to him even when a schoolboy as a paradise...

> Once on the brow of yonder Hill I stopped,
> While I was yet a School-boy (of what age
> I cannot well remember, but the hour
> I well remember though the year be gone),
> And with a sudden influx overcome
> At sight of this seclusion, I forgot
> My haste – for hasty had my footsteps been,
> As boyish my pursuits – (and sighing said),

186

"What happy fortune were it here to live!
And if I thought of dying, if a thought
Of mortal separation could come in
With paradise before me, here to die."
In this sense the paradisal image of Grasmere was fundamental to the
life that he and his sister intended to live there, a life of virtuous
economy made possible by the small legacy (of 1795) from his school
fellow Raisley Calvert.

In fact, the essential constituent of the plan was that Wordsworth
should encounter the common people and be able to draw upon the
resources of anecdote and hidden drama contained in their lives. The
poem *Michael* (1800), tracing the decline of a statesman shepherd family
in the local image of an unfinished sheepfold, was one of the first
productions of the Grasmere period, and with the prose Prefaces to the
Lyrical Ballads in which Wordsworth proclaimed the aesthetic of
vernacular diction, is characteristic of his intentions. Dorothy's record of
the babble of common life passing outside Dove Cottage – 'Matthew
Jobson's lost a cow. Tom Nichol has two good horses strayed. Jim Jones'
cow's brokken her horn' – was made to provide material for her brother's
work.

187

JOSEPH FARINGTON
183 Grasmere from Dunmail Raise 1777
    Pen, pencil and wash
    32.5 x 47.5 cm.
    Trustees of Dove Cottage
Farington's view of Grasmere, 12 June
1777, precisely and deliberately
illustrates the image identified by Gray
as a 'little unsuspected paradise'.

FRANCIS TOWNE
184 Grasmere from the
    Rydal Road 1786
    Watercolour 21.2 x 34 cm.
    Birmingham Museum and
    Art Gallery,

J. WHITE ABBOTT 1763-1851
185 Helm Crag on Grasmere Lake 1791
    Watercolour 18.5 x 29.2 cm.
    Trustees of Dove Cottage

JULIUS CAESAR IBBETSON 1759-1817
186 Grasmere 1801
    Oil on canvas
    66.5 x 83.2 cm.
    Private Collection courtesy of John
    Mitchell and Son

PETER DE WINT 1784-1849
187 Grasmere and Helm Crag c. 1821-30
    Oil on canvas 66 x 96.5 cm.
    Leeds City Art Gallery

188 Grasmere, Church and Village with
  o Helm Crag c. 1821
     Watercolour 19.4 x 48 cm.
     Victoria and Albert Museum
     E2423-1928

GEORGE FENNEL ROBSON 1788-1833
189 View of Grasmere from
  o Red Bank 1831
     Watercolour 42.7 x 81.5 cm.
     Trustees of Dove Cottage

WORDSWORTH AS GUIDE

Wilkinson, a pluralist clergyman, born at Carlisle, married locally in 1788 and was therefore able to spend much time in the Lake District, at Ormathwaite under Skiddaw, until he moved to Norfolk as Rector of East and West Wretham in 1804. Five years later, for his projected publication of the *Select Views*, he pressed Wordsworth and Coleridge to supply him with a suitable text. Wordsworth, reluctantly because he wished not to crowd the market against his closer acquaintance William Green, supplied the letterpress anonymously. After revision, expansion and intermediate publication with *The River Duddon* sonnets of 1820, the work came out in 1822 as an independent book. Despite its genesis as the accompaniment to a series of pictures, the *Guide* differed from West and from the earlier guides, in pressing a very different, non-pictorial, method of looking at the landscape.

190

JOSEPH WILKINSON 1764–1831

190 Select Views in Cumberland, Westmorland and Lancashire
Ackermann London 1810
Issued in 12 parts; 48 soft ground etchings by W. T. Wells coloured and uncoloured
Trustees of Dove Cottage

191 Another copy, showing printed paper covers
King's College Cambridge Bicknell Collection

WILLIAM WORDSWORTH

192 A Description of the Scenery of the Lakes in the North of England
Third edition (now published separately) with Additions and illustrative Remarks upon the Scenery of the Alps London 1822
Trustees of Dove Cottage

Wordsworth's *Guide* underwent continuous revision and expansion in the five editions supervised by him, as well as those published by John Hudson from 1842. It was the medium through which Wordsworth expressed his committed interest in the visual, long after he had, as a poet and sage, publicly relegated the visual arts – their discipline and critical techniques – to a lower order of human discourse. His note to *Descriptive Sketches* of 1793 is part of the reaction against pictorialism in the 1790's, and marginally anticipates Uvedale Price's *Essays* of 1794 which did much to rehabilitate the Picturesque, to rescue its terminology and to alter its focus. Wordsworth wrote:

> 'I had once given to these sketches the title of Picturesque; but the Alps are insulted in applying to them that term. Whoever, in attempting to describe their sublime features, should confine himself to the cold rules of painting would give his reader but a very imperfect idea of those emotions which they have the irresistible power of communicating to the most impassive imaginations. The fact is, that controuling influence, which distinguishes the Alps from all other scenery, is derived from images which disdain the pencil. Had I wished to make a picture of this scene I had thrown much less light into it. But I consulted nature and my feelings. The ideas excited by the stormy sunset I am here describing owed their sublimity to that deluge of light, or rather of fire, in which nature had wrapped the immense forms around me; and intrusion of shade, by destroying the unity of the impression, had necessarily diminished its grandeur.'

As a text, Wordsworth's *Guide* belongs to the aesthetic moment of 1810, the year in which he first visited Uvedale Price at Foxley in Herefordshire, and to the succeeding decades during which, as Walter Scott pointed out, the conservative, historicising and non-interventionist aesthetic pioneered by Price and Knight, became established. Wordsworth was an intensely visual person, the friend of painters and the regular correspondent of Sir George Beaumont in matters of visual theory and criticism. He was the architect of Beaumont's winter garden at Coleorton and the letters written in connection with the project in the years 1805-7 stand as one of the main texts of high Picturesque garden design. His own garden at Dove Cottage was itself a major artefact of Picturesque garden design, and prepared the way for the later work at Rydal Mount, in the full 'architectural' idiom associated with Price's doctrine. It is important to understand and give the proper weight to this side of Wordsworth's nature, not only as a matter of aesthetic pathology, but because Wordsworth was so influential, and his *Guide* became the standard work on the visual qualities of the Lake District. The architectural axioms of building and gardening in the Lake District for the next hundred years were established by the *Guide*.

The Wordsworthian shift in his approach to landscape, from critical pictorialism to a sense of responsibilty for its right development and careful conservation, thus become normative in the culture, inspiring successive generations down to the present. On this basis, his great poetic labour, in which he struggled to find a language adequate to his sense of 'Something far more deeply interfused', and in which he traced the growth of his mind through moments of moral éclaircissement in the landscape, provide texts to justify high expectations of the educative or healing power of Nature. Wordsworth is thus fundamental to the whole post-pictorial culture of landscape in England.

DOVE COTTAGE

Until Humphry Repton published views of his own house, the Hare Street Cottage, in 1816, the idea that the cottage, especially in a constricted site, close to a road and with other houses pressing in, could be the creation of an aesthetically sophisticated sensibility, was not widespread. Admiration of the cottage as the unconsidered outcome of peasant existence, was part of Picturesque doctrine, and had a pre-history in the Pastoral tradition, but the deliberate construction of a cottage and garden adapted to the existence of scholar-gentlemen was a characteristic development of the early 19th century. The work of the Wordsworths at Dove Cottage in 1800 was therefore highly original. They brought into the garden the local flora, transplanted from the lake and fell side, from the woodlands and from the gardens of the local farms and cottages where traditionally cultivated plants flourished. There was an emphasis on minute effects – Dorothy Wordsworth was especially interested in mosses – and on the construction of sheltered secreted places surrounded

194

by trees, bushes and climbing and trailing plants. On the steeply sloping site of Dove Cottage, the emphasis was vertical, and the effects were close to the eye, intended to form a harmony with the carefully managed views through the leafage over Grasmere to Red Bank and Silver Howe. The deliberation and shared responsiblity for the work between William and Dorothy Wordsworth emerges repeatedly in the Grasmere Journal, as when William returns late in the evening of 7 June 1800, and he and Dorothy then stay up till 4 am so that he might 'see our improvements'.

193

AMOS GREEN 1735-1807
193 Dove Cottage
Watercolour 13.1 x 20.3 cm.
Trustees of Dove Cottage

194 Dove Cottage from the road
May 1984
Photograph David Lyons

195 View down the garden towards
○ the garden door June 1984
Photograph David Lyons
The Wordsworths' provision of this door effectively brings the garden into the house, lighting the staircase, and creating a view of the garden which would have been unthinkable as a fine view before the 1790's.

196 From the interior staircase into
the garden June 1984
Photograph David Lyons

197 Steps up the garden including
○ the Bower May 1984
Photograph David Lyons

198 Fireplace in the sitting room 1984
Photograph David Lyons
The site of intense colloquy between Wordsworth, Coleridge and others of the British cultural élite, as Dove Cottage became the site where the various influences on British romanticism, from France, Switzerland, Germany, America, and from the vernacular resources of Britain itself, intersected.

199 The kitchen 1984
Photograph David Lyons
The sense of personal contact with the real world through the experience of work – household chores – was essential to Dove Cottage existence.

RYDAL HALL AND RYDAL MOUNT

The seat of the Flemings who, since the mid seventeenth century, had occupied the hall, improving its gardens and park, and providing in the heart of the Lake District a continuous history of high aesthetic consciousness, merely augmented by the Arcadian cult of the late eighteenth century. The continuity of the Pastoral – itself a rediscovery by Renaissance scholars of the Virgilian ethos – connects at Rydal Hall the sixteenth with the nineteenth century; and the pre-history of the Picturesque interest in close-up, naturally 'composed' views, is demonstrated by the so called Summer House constructed, or even re constructed, by Sir Daniel Fleming in 1668. The romantic use of landscape, and of dim enclosed spaces to induce thought, can be traced back here to the Renaissance Grotto, and thence to Plato's cave. When in 1813 Wordsworth came to Rydal Mount, the 'minor' neighbouring house to the Hall, his sense that anything he did should be consistent with the natural history of the locality would be able to draw nourishment from this deeply established tradition of landscape improvement at Rydal.

203

RYDAL MOUNT Formerly the house of the Knotts, and like Rydal Hall, the seat of a family that had participated fully in the culture since the mid-seventeenth century. The house was 'turned' from its original eastern orientation towards the south west and the Windermere view in about 1750, and in the 1770's John Knott had planned to put an obelisk on the top of Orrest Head and a pyramid on Loughrigg to complete the view from the house. Such plans for Poussinesque, Arcadian improvements to the landscape narrowly anticipate the works of Thomas English at Belle Isle. From the 1780's the house was let occasionally to Daniel Daulby (see no. 106), a practising Arcadian.

After Daulby's death another Liverpool business man, Ford North, bought Rydal Mount from the Knott family trustees. He quarrelled with the Flemings of Rydal Hall about the oaks. They, as lords of the manor, exercised their hereditary rights over the felling of timber trees as firmly as they controlled building development in their domain, but between them, the squabbling Flemings and Ford North cut down all the oaks on Nab Scar above the lake. Eventually the Flemings bought North out at cost, and Rydal Mount was leased for a period of twelve years to Wordsworth in 1813.

The Wordsworths, William and his wife Mary, with Dorothy and the children, were anxious to leave Grasmere, the sad scene of the recent death of two of their five children. Rydal Mount was therefore the place in which they reconstructed their domestic life. As tenants, there was little they could do with the house, but the garden became the focus of all Wordsworth's busy interest in the visual and profound urge to express himself in the landscape arts.

JOSEPH FARINGTON
200 View of Rydal near Ambleside
    Chalks and wash 40 x 56 cm.
    Private Collection
The view, taken by Farington on one of his early visits in the 1770's, shows the Hall before it was re cased in the classicising idiom of the 1780's and 90's, and before it was 'turned' to face the view towards Windemere. His view is still that of Gray in 1769 – 'a large old fashioned fabrick, rounded with wood'.

201 Rydal Lower Fall
    Black chalk 43.8 x 56.7 cm.
    Jonathan Wordsworth
The view from the summer house.

202 Bridge at Rydal
    Watercolour
    38.6 x 57 cm.
    Birmingham Museum and
    Art Gallery

203 Rydal Hall c. 1860
    Photograph Francis Frith
    series no. 1684
    Victoria and Albert Museum

204 The Summer House: view through
  O the house and window June 1984
    Photograph David Lyons

200

JOSEPH WRIGHT of Derby 1734-97
205 Rydal Lower Fall
  O Oil on canvas 76 x 95.2 cm.
    Derby Museums and Art Gallery

JOHN RATHBONE c. 1750-1807
206 Rydal Bridge
    Oil on canvas 44.7 x 59.5 cm.
    Victoria and Albert Musuem
    Dyce 56
This is Pelter Bridge, part of the

landscape accompaniments of Rydal Hall and Rydal Mount, visible from each before the trees grew up. The Rathbone view was traditionally attributed to Ibbetson, who came to Rydal soon after the death at Rydal Mount of Daniel Daulby, and took up the Arcadian pastoral idiom promoted by Daulby and realised previously for him by Thomas Chubbard. The grounds for the attribution to Rathbone are slight.

207 Rydal Mount c. 1880
   Photograph Francis Frith
   Series no. 3962
   Victoria and Albert Museum

THOMAS CHUBBARD C. 1738-1809
Said to have been born in Liverpool, and certainly having important patronage in that town, he came to the Lake District in the suite of Daniel Daulby (see no. 106). He and Ibbetson had some professional contact as leaders of art education and exhibitions in Liverpool in the 1770's and 1780's.

   The Rydal Album c. 1796-8
208 – open at *The Mount Rydal*
   Trustees of Dove Cottage
Many of the sheets in this book reproduce views from West's Stations on Windermere, including two that show the house on Belle Isle and Brathay Hall at the head of the lake. More importantly, the book, which was in the possession of the Daulby family and was presumably compiled for them, is a record of the consciously Arcadian life designed by them for their retirement at Rydal. Thus we see Mrs. Daulby milking cows in the field adjoining Rydal Mount, and the Lady Oak – symbolic of the oaks which grew all over Nab Scar and which contributed essentially to the Arcadian character of the landscape.
   Another study takes the eponymous Mount of Rydal as its subject, the ornamental mound constructed by the Knotts as a viewing platform, and as a formal geometrical motif for the view from the house in the 1770's.

209 – photograph View from Rydal Mount, Mrs Daulby as a Milkmaid

210 – photograph Rydal Mount from the Lady Oak.

   WILLIAM GREEN
211 Oak Tree at Rydal 11 September 1806
   Pencil
   Victoria and Albert Museum

WORDSWORTH AS GARDENER

Conservation and respectful historicism are the key elements of Uvedale Price's landscape doctrine. Wordsworth, even more insistently than his mentor, argued that a house should harmonise with its surroundings and be in keeping with the traditions of the locality. Terraces, with their function of supporting and managing the relation of a house to the landscape, especially on a sloping site, were technically fundamental to the Picturesque garden. At Rydal he came into a landscape with a long continuous history of improvement already stamped upon it. The definitive features of the design, the Mount, Pelter Bridge, the prospect over Rydal towards Windermere, and above all the First Terrace, were in position. Wordsworth simply extended, elaborated and adorned what he came upon, making thus in sympathy with its history one of the most important new gardens of the early 19th century.

218

212 The Lawn at Rydal Mount July 1984
    Photograph David Lyons

The old kitchen garden was the first thing Wordsworth went to work on at Rydal Mount. Thirty years later he recalled:

> 'This lawn is a sloping one approaching the kitchen-garden, and was made out of it. Hundreds of times have I watched the dancing of shadows amid a press of sunshine, and other beautiful appearances of light and shade, flowers and shrubs'.

In accordance with Picturesque doctrine, however, the kitchen garden remained absolutely integral to the overall design, helping to link the house visually with its surroundings through the graded relationship of terraces, parterres, lawns, shrubberies, fields and woodlands. Again, though further from the house, the kitchen garden with its vicissitudes of productivity, remained a high point of consciousness, not quite as vivid, but as constant as it had been at Dove Cottage.

213 The First Terrace: the Steps
 July 1984
 Photograph David Lyons
 To the First Terrace he added the Far
 Terrace, marking the transition with
 a summer house or bower.

214 The First Terrace: transition to the
 narrow Far Terrace July 1984
 Photograph David Lyons

215 The Green Terrace: Dora's Field
 July 1984
 Photograph David Lyons

216 Miss Fenwick's Terrace: from below
 July 1984
 Photograph David Lyons

In March 1826 Wordsworth purchased
the piece of land now known as Dora's
Field, and by 1830 was:
> 'making a Green Terrace, that
> commands a beautiful view over
> our two Lakes Rydal and
> Windermere, and more than two
> miles of intervening vale with the
> stream visible by glimpses, flowing
> through it'.

The Green Terrace is especially
associated with Dorothy Wordsworth
who, after crippling illness settled on her
in 1835, was pushed to and fro in her
special carriage on its easy slopes.

JOHN HARDEN
217 Dorothy Wordsworth in her invalid
 chair 25 August 1842
 Pen and ink 11.4 x 18.1 cm.
 Abbot Hall Art Gallery
Her journal records the trance-like
private and intensely selective awareness
of their surroundings that the
Wordsworths cultivated in themselves at
Rydal as they had at Grasmere:
> 'Had a delightful airing (1½ hours)
> on green Terrace with James alone –
> Wm lying on grass plot shaded with
> Umbrella &c I passed him
> unperceived of him, & not

perceiving him though close to him.
The day charming – a newly fledged
Thrush could but fly to the top of
the wall – The little wren very
busy...' 24 May 1834

The last of the three terraces was built
in the late 1830's, partly for the benefit
of the family friend Isabella Fenwick,
who could not manage the steps of the
First nor the slopes of the Green Terrace.
Miss Fenwick's Terrace opens out of the
large drawing room at the western end
of the house.

Its relatively smooth surface was
especially conducive to the Poet's own
ruminative, oral style of composition –
his 'bumming' murmurous rehearsal of
lines as he paced up and down.

WILLIAM WESTALL 1781-1850
218 The Garden at Rydal Mount 1831
 Watercolour from Dora's Album
 page size 11.5 x 13.1 cm.
 Trustees of Dove Cottage

219 Rydal from 'Mr Wordsworth's
 Field' (Dora's Field)
 Aquatint, one of a series of
 panoramic views of the Lakes
 Ackermann 1831-9
 Trustees of Dove Cottage

220 Room at Rydal Mount 1840
 Lithograph from *Views of the Lake
 Country To Illustrate the Poems of W.
 Wordsworth Esq.*, London Moxon
 1840
 Trustees of Dove Cottage

220

WORDSWORTH AS BUILDER

From the start the condition of Rydal Mount, especially the back part of the house, was unsatisfactory. Wordsworth's eloquence of complaint to Lady Fleming, his landlady, perhaps contributed to a slight distancing between them, and in 1825 it became known that she had a fancy to instal members of her own family or social group, or even her land agent, in the house. Wordsworth accordingly bought Dora's Field with the intention of building upon it, if Lady Fleming, having perhaps rendered the greatest living English poet homeless, could be prevailed upon to enfranchise the land for building.

George Webster, younger son of the distinguished Kendal family firm of architects, which had been deeply involved in the spread of Arcadian villas through Cumbria in the last quarter of the eighteenth century, was his architect. The design for Wordsworth is a critical document in the shift during the 1820's from the straightforward classical designs of the first wave of building to the Picturesque historic styles of the second. The re-modelling of Croft Lodge in 1828 and the new Coniston Waterhead built by the Knotts before 1822 were the achieved structures in the new idiom. Wordsworth's Rydal house would have been a different, and in some ways more influential, contribution to the same aesthetic.

Webster must have listened carefully to his client and been readily sympathetic, to have linked with such success the elements of timeless

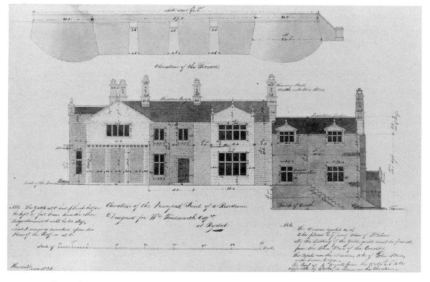

vernacular (the round chimneys) with Jacobean mullioned windows, ball and spike finials to the roof line, and studded door, with a Roman colonade and Italianate terracing. Perhaps only at Rydal could such a rich eclecticism have precise local antecedents, and Webster's house seems designed as a visual catalogue of motifs borrowed from the seventeenth and eighteenth century developments at Rydal Hall and Rydal Mount.

As a small house, smaller than anything else in the area that could be compared with it in deliberate architectural quality, and much smaller than Italianate houses such as Webster's later Belsfield (1840),
the Rydal house would have modelled for the villas erected for the bourgeois intellectuals such as Thomas Arnold and Harriet Martineau, in the second quarter of the century.

GEORGE WEBSTER 1797-1864
221 Design for the main elevation of a house for Wordsworth 1827
Ink and watercolour 29.5 x 47.8 cm.
Trustees of Dove Cottage

B. R. HAYDON 1786-1846
222 Wordsworth on Helvellyn 1842
○ Oil on canvas 1244 x 991 cm.
National Portrait Gallery

WORDSWORTH THE SAGE

In the opening of the eighth book of his epic autobiography, *The Prelude*, Wordsworth takes as his theme: love of nature leading to love of mankind. The introductory image is of Grasmere Vale, enclosed within its green mountain pastures, and animated with the myriad business of its annual fair. Helvellyn presides:

Immense
Is the recess, the circumambient world
Magnificent, by which they are embraced.
They move about upon the soft green turf;
How little they, they and their doings, seem,
And all that they can further or obstruct!
Through utter weakness pitiably dear,
As tender infants are: and yet how great!
For all things serve them; them the morning light
Loves, as it glistens on the silent rocks, which now from high
Look down upon them; the reposing clouds,
The wild brooks prattling from invisible haunts;
And old Helvellyn, conscious of the stir
Which animates this day their calm abode.
The Prelude, 1850, VIII, 55-69

Shortly after writing this passage Wordsworth happened in 1806 to meet Constable in the Lake District: in his conversation he gave a clue, vital to us if not to Constable, about a mental predicament that had haunted him from his schooldays. Wordsworth's comments as remembered by Constable are recorded in Farington's Diary 12 December 1807, over a year after their meeting:

Constable remarked upon the high opinion Wordsworth entertains of Himself. He told Constable that while He was a Boy going to Hawkshead School, His mind was often so possessed with images so lost in extraordinary conceptions, that He has held by a wall not knowing but He was part of it. – He also desired a Lady, Mrs. Loyd, near Windermere when Constable was present to notice the singular formation of His Skull. – Coleridge remarked that this was the effect of intense thinking. – I observed to Constable if so, He must have thought in His Mother's womb.

What Constable does not recognise, but we can, is that one of Wordsworth's nightmares is here expressed: the activity of his mind was so intense that he feared he might become insensible to the outside world, and that he would be, like Milton, a blind poet. As a young man Wordsworth corrected this concern with the overactive internal imagination by actively seeking images from the matter-of-fact world that was ordinarily about him. As he expresses it in 'Tintern Abbey':

> The mountain, and the deep and gloomy wood,
> Their colours and their forms, were then to me
> An Appetite...

In those early times, such scenes did not need 'any interest/Unborrowed from the eye'.

It can be misleading, as well as helpful, to call Wordsworth a 'Nature Poet'. As his intellect matured, he came to believe that views of the external world only had meaning in terms of the interior life of the beholder; perception as a creative act became his real interest. Nothing more easily shows this than his understanding of the act, and one might say art, of memory – for Wordsworth discovered in the well of memory the founts that feed every man. The analysis in *The Prelude* Book XI, of the Spots of Time – those key memories – was to demonstrate that there is an architecture in such reconstructed episodes from one's past, most of all from one's childhood, which are the bastion of individuality. Wordsworth recognised that the urgency of such images is that they are vision, are the fountain light of all our days. Thus, the boy who steals the boat on Ullswater and then experiences the mountain lifting up its head in a paternal remonstrance, is living in a beneficent world of fear and love that gives fit tutelage: the educative power of nature is thus impressively experienced.

Human teachers (not least through books) could only add emphasis to the lesson for the poet envisages a world where a boy responds to natural forces, great natural potentates, or secularised principalities and powers. Wordsworth famously describes the boy who imitated the hooting of owls, and he records that in the gaps between the hootings of the boy and of the owls, the mountains and all the lakeland scenery pass *far* into the boy's heart; it was De Quincey who first noted that the key word is 'far'.

> And, when there came a pause
> Of silence such as baffled his best skill:
> Then sometimes, in that silence, while he hung
> Listening, a gentle shock of mild surprise
> Has carried far into his heart the voice
> Of mountain-torrents; or the visible scene
> Would enter unawares into his mind
> With all its solemn imagery, its rocks,

Its woods, and that uncertain heaven received
Into the bosom of the steady lake.

Wordsworth's phrasing often implies that the mental world itself is physically immense, that thus it is that the mind of man is appropriately married to this vast and 'goodly universe' – a consummation devoutly to be known and reverenced:

The darkest pit of lowest Erebus,
Nor aught of blinder vacancy, scooped out
By help of dreams – can breed such fear and awe
As fall upon us often when we look
Into our Minds, into the Mind of Man –
My haunt, and the main region of my song.
– Beauty – a living Presence of the earth,
Surpassing the most fair ideal Forms
Which craft of delicate Spirits hath composed
From earth's materials – waits upon my steps;
Pitches her tents before me as I move,
An hourly neighbour. Paradise, and groves
Elysian, Fortunate Fields – like those of old
Sought in the Atlantic Main – why should they be
A history only of departed things,
Or a mere fiction of what never was?
For the discerning intellect of Man,
When wedded to this goodly universe
In love and holy passion, shall find these
A simple produce of the common day.
– I, long before the blissful hour arrives,
Would chant, in lonely peace, the spousal verse
Of this great consummation: – and, by words
Which speak of nothing more than what we are.
Would I arouse the sensual from their sleep
Of Death, and win the vacant and the vain
To noble raptures; while my voice proclaims
How exquisitely the individual Mind
(And the progressive powers perhaps no less
Of the whole species) to the external World
Is fitted:– and how exquisitely, too –
Theme this but little heard of among men –
The external World is fitted to the Mind;
And the creation (by no lower name
Can it be called) which they with blended might
Accomplish:– this is our high argument.

(Preface to *The Excursion* 1814, 35-71)

RUSKIN AT CONISTON

The image of the Victorian Sage is not easy to hold still, though the characteristic visual invention of the mid-nineteenth century, the photograph, isolated that problem and opened up in its solution the possibility of an objective realism in the arts. Thus photographs of the great men, caught in the midst of their daily routine, among their friends, sitting on terraces, walking in the shrubberies of the villa gardens of the high Picturesque, seem to offer a more real and a sharper insight into the nature of their social authority than the static, composed, pictorial view of the painted portrait or the studio photograph. Yet there is a tradition of Sage portraiture in the nineteenth century, that of the Author in his Study, which, having a long iconographic history stretching back to images of St Jerome in his study, focusses an otherwise unseen aspect of the Sage's life: his solitary scholarship, the long hours of

223

reading and the painful labour over drafts of symphonic prose.

By the mid-nineteenth century the Lake District, filling with the villas of the intellectual and industrial bourgeoisie, had become a place of reflection, thought, and the attainment of wisdom, a place to which, as to Helvellyn itself, the hubbub of human sound reached up in a form conducive to humanitarian sympathy. In *The Prelude* Wordsworth had described how the lessons of human affection were prompted by the 'moral power' of the landscape, and led to more complicated insights than were contained in the simple structural principles of the classical landscape tradition – or even in the sharpest sensual apprehension of colour or form. The same lessons were borne in equally upon Ruskin, sitting self tortured and alone in the early morning, addressing the vast proletarian audience that he hoped to reach from his study at Brantwood, and thinking compulsively of those few people who had meant most to him, and were dead.

'Morning breaks as I write, along these Coniston Fells, and the level mists, motionless, and grey beneath the rose of the moorlands, veil the lower woods, and the sleeping village, and the long lawns by the lake-shore.

Oh, that some one had but told me, in my youth, when all my heart seemed to be set on these colours and clouds, that appear for a little while and then vanish away, how little my love of them would serve me, when the silence of lawn and wood in the dews of the morning should be completed; and all my thoughts should be of those whom, by neither (wood nor lawn), I was to meet more!' 12 February 1878.

225

W. G. COLLINGWOOD
223 Ruskin and his Study at Brantwood
1882
Oil on canvas
The Ruskin Museum Coniston

ARTHUR SEVERN
224 Ruskin's Bedroom
23 April 1900
Watercolour
The Brantwood Educational Trust

J. RUSKIN
225 Self-portrait 1873/4
Pencil 23 x 20.5 cm.
Brantwood Educational Trust
(no. 991)

226 Fixed cloud over Coniston Old Man
9 April 1875
Watercolour
Ruskin Museum Coniston (no. 17)

227 Morning cloud at Consiton 1877
○ Watercolour 14 x 21.5 cm.
Ruskin Museum Coniston (no. 18)

ALEX MACDONALD
228 View from the Study at Brantwood
4.30 am. 3 August 1880
Watercolour
The Ruskin Museum Coniston

229 Ruskin at Brantwood 1872
Photograph anonymous
The Ruskin Museum Coniston

230 Ruskin and Joan Seven in Ruskin's
boat Jumping Jenny
Photograph anonymous
The Ruskin Museum Coniston

2.

RUSKIN AND THE LAKE DISTRICT

Ruskin first visited the Lakes in 1824 at the age of 5. It must have been on
this trip that, as he recorded in *Modern Painters*, he was taken by his nurse
to Friar's Crag on Derwentwater to see the famous bowl of lake, islands
and surrounding hills. Prophetically, what he noticed was the minute
foreground effect –

> 'the intense joy, mingled with awe, that I had in looking through the
> hollows in the mossy roots, over the crag into the dark lake, has ever
> associated itself more or less with twining roots of trees ever since.'

That experience led on to moments in later life, such as that at
Fontainebleau in 1842, when he realised the principle of 'natural
composition', that objects in nature 'composed themselves by finer laws
than any known of man'. This rejection of 'pictorialism' was shared by
those, painters as well as writers, who turned away similarly from the
prospect or panorama towards the close-up view or the telescopically
isolated distance. The doctrine deriving from this that elevates accuracy
of observation and exactness of draughtsmanship, the doctrine of 'added
truth' in the painting of detail, was Ruskin's main contribution to the
aesthetics of painting in the 1850's, when he wrote the third volume of
Modern Painters and publicly defended Pre-Raphaelitism. At least partly
under his influence and certainly with the weight of his approval, the
mode of vision contained in the romantic cult of the sketch or study
became a public part of the educated Englishman's aesthetic
consciousness.

231 Manuscript of 1830 Tour
The Ruskin Museum Coniston
Subsequent trips to the Lake District in 1830 and 1837 produced other
impressions crucial to Ruskin's later life. In 1830 he kept a journal with

his cousin Mary Richardson who travelled with the family, and he
adapted it after his return into the long jocular poem 'The Iteriad'.
Collingwood, Ruskin's friend and authoritative biographer, testifies that
when, in 1871, Ruskin was desperately sick and thinking of finding some
withdrawn place for rest, his thoughts turned to the 1830 tour and put
him in mind of Coniston.

In 1837 his sketchbook and drawings of buildings on separate sheets
provided material for his first important publication *The Poetry of
Architecture*, contributed as articles to J. C. Loudon's *Architectural
Magazine* between November 1837 and December 1838.

J. RUSKIN
232 Sketch book for 1837
The Ruskin Museum Coniston

233 Troutbeck Cottages 7 August 1837
Pencil
The Brantwood Educational Trust

Apart from a few days at Kendal, Low Wood and Keswick in July
1838, again en route to Scotland, Ruskin did not go north again until
1847, for the first time without his parents. The visit was brief. The next
year, on honeymoon touring southward from his marriage in Perthshire,
he and his wife stayed for about ten days at Keswick. Nineteen years
later, on his own again, he spent most of July and August in Keswick,
and found many things sadly changed. His impression of the Low Wood
where he had often stayed with his parents, drove him quickly out: 'Low
Wood was too noisy and fashionable – (Manchester fashion) for me, so I
drove over here yesterday and got a lovely little corner parlour.' This was
at Cloudsdale's Crown Hotel at Bowness, but the bustle of that rapidly
developing centre soon also drove him out; after a flying visit of two
days over the border into Scotland he took a look at the new Keswick
Hotel, built by the railway company and connected to the station by a
covered way, and retreated quickly to private rooms by Bassenthwaite.
He lamented generally the changes brought about by the building boom,
and wrote to his mother about another of the family's favourite hotels,
the Waterhead at Coniston:

'(It) exists no more. Its place is grown over with smooth park grass
... and a quarter of a mile down the lake a vast hotel built on the
railroad station style, making up I suppose its fifty or eighty beds,
with coffee room, smoking room and every other pestilent and
devilish Yankeeism that money can buy or speculation plan...'

'I rowed up the Brathay. The stones we used to drift upon are all
taken away and until one reaches the quite impassable rapid, all is
smooth and like the Thames – for the pleasure boats of the villas...'
It was Ruskin's last trip before he himself became a resident, living
on the lakeside at Coniston, moving stones to build a harbour for his
boats, in a house that grew from being a fair example of the local
Cumbrian types that he admired, into a strange and specialised
version of the bourgeouis villa. He arrived there on 12 September

1871, and described his acquisition to Thomas Carlyle as ...
'a bit of steep hillside, facing west ... The slope is half copse, half
moor and rock – a pretty field beneath, less steep – a white
two-storied cottage, and a bank of turf in front of it; – then a narrow
mountain road and on the other side of that ... my neighbour's field,
to the water's edge'.

234 The Low Wood Hotel c. 1870
  Photograph Francis Frith Series
  Victoria and Albert Museum

  J. RUSKIN
235 Brantwood from the edge
 O of Coniston
  Pencil and wash 17.2 x 24.6 cm.
  The Brantwood Educational Trust
Ruskin's note on this drawing is that it
was made 'before additions', that is,
more or less as he first saw the house
when he came to it in September 1871

234

BRANTWOOD

It is of major interest that the most innovative lay critic of architecture in
the nineteenth century, in a period richly endowed with brilliant English
architects considerably inspired by his own teaching and in an area richly
endowed with materials and a craft tradition that he admired intensely,
should have chosen to adapt an existing 'cottage' to his needs rather than
to build new from the ground up. The reasons are foreshadowed in *The
Poetry of Architecture*, and are contained in a concept that he identified in
that work as the Cottage Villa.

Ruskin's admiration for cottages was anchored in Picturesque
aesthetics, and like the Picturesque writers he recognised in the Cottage
an image of profound 'organic' rightness, in which the lessons of
humility, of suiting one's house and oneself to their proper situation,
were perfectly expressed. In the achievement of this, the absence of taste,
of conscious architecture, was essential – any operation of taste such as
whitewashing ruined the effect. Turning to the proprieties of building
for the upper classes in mountainous districts, Ruskin identified the Lake
District as especially suitable for settlement, but rejected the classicising
architecture of the late eighteenth century villa developments on the lakes
as ostentatious and intrusive.

'For these reasons, the cottage-villa, rather than the mansion, is to be
preferred among our hills.'
The cottage-villa, the hybrid, or conversion of the basic upland cottage
to the needs of the upper classes, thus offered a way forward. By
conversion, the bourgeois element, with its disabling burden of aesthetic

and moral consciousness, could acquire the natural rightness and wholeness with surroundings that belonged to the cottage.

> 'The house must *not* be a noun substantive, it must not stand by itself, it must be part and parcel of a proportioned whole . . . (he who see it should be) impressed with a feeling of universal energy, pervading with its beauty of unanimity all life and all inanimation, all forces of stillness or motion, all presences of silence or sound.'

By acquiring Brantwood, Collingwood tells us, and adapting it to his use, Ruskin hoped to achieve some such sense of rightness and peace, some refuge from his appalling sense of horrors beyond, and within himself.

WORK AT BRANTWOOD

'Nature,' Ruskin wrote in *The Poetry of Architecture*, 'has set aside her sublime bits for us to feel and think in . . . all that we ought to do in the hill villa is, to adapt it for the habitation of a man of the highest faculties of perception and feeling'.

The Ruskin of 1871, the year in which he bought Brantwood, was very far from retired. His house was to be an additional resource to supply the energies consumed in his public life. His political work, largely economic in its focus during the 1860's, was developed in 1871 by the endowment of his Guild of St George, founded to be the instrument of his social intervention. At his study window at Brantwood, Ruskin increased his intellectual, moral and material commitment to post–Chartist and pre–Socialist radicalism. The Plague Wind of the Nineteenth Century – the corrupt effluvia of urban industrial capitalism – blew as visibly across the Coniston Fells as it hung over the streets of London, Birmingham and Manchester.

The characteristic literary works of Brantwood are therefore *Fors Clavigera*, the letters to the workmen and labourers of Britain, and the collected papers of *Deucalion* and *Proserpina* in which he attempted to set out a reformed methodology of natural history for the education and benefit of the rising generation.

236 Geological Sample: Copper ore with pyrites from Wetherham
    The Ruskin Museum Coniston

The role of geology in the growth of Ruskin's mind was fundamental. His acquaintance with developments in glacial theory of the 1840's and 1850's, which contradicted the Biblical accounts of Creation and Flood, was particularly unsettling to a mind educated in the strict evangelical fundamentalist tradition, whereby the literal truth of revelation in the Bible was a seamless garment unravelled by a single tear.

> 'You speak of the flimsiness of your own faith. Mine, which was never strong, is being beaten into mere gold leaf, and flutters in weak rags from the letter of its old forms; but the only letters it can hold by at all are the old Evangelical formulae. If only the Geologists would let me alone, I could do very well, but those dreadful Hammers! I hear the clink of them at the end of every cadence of the Bible

verses.'

In the Brantwood studies, some of which, such as 'Yewdale and its Streams', derive specifically from the glaciated and waterworn Lake District landscape, Ruskin sought out the means to a natural history of the earth which would affirm the sculptural mystery of continuous Creation. From the evidences of cyclical and non-catastrophic inundation, he could construct an equivalent parable of Mercy and Redemption, and he called his collected studies accordingly *Deucalion*, in allusion to the Greek Noah, son of Prometheus, who saved himself and his wife from Jupiter's Flood by taking refuge on Parnassus.

241

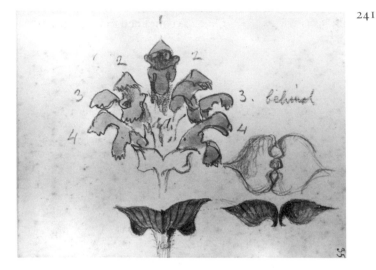

237 Study of a Sycamore 1875
    Watercolour 19 x 14 cm.
    The Brantwood Educational Trust

238 Study of Wood Sorrel
    (Oxalis acetosella)
    Watercolour 11.9 x 8.6 cm. (sight)
    Brantwood Educational Trust 1419

239 Study of a petal of Wood Sorrel
    Watercolour 11.9 x 8.6 cm. (sight)
    Brantwood Educational Trust

240 Study of a flower, apparently
    Self-Heal (Prunella vulgaris)
    Watercolour 13.6 x 9.1 cm. (sight)
    Brantwood Educational Trust 1270

241 Analytical study of the above
    Watercolour 8.5 x 10.4 cm. (sight)
    Brantwood Educational Trust

238

A similar theme of redemption is signalled in the title of the concurrent Brantwood studies – *Proserpina* (the Latin form of the Greek Persephone), symbolic figure of the returning Spring. This is Ruskin's proposal for a new botanic taxonomy freed of silly Latinism – Ruskin's mockery of Latin plant names is delicious – and independent of the new Darwinian-scientific orthodoxy which taught, for example, that the flower was beautiful in order to attract insects, to fertilise it and achieve genetic diversity through sexual reproduction. Ruskin on the contrary proposed that the 'flower is the end of the seed, – not the seed of the flower'.

It was Ruskin's point that the necessary teaching for children, and for those who would be as wise as children, was contained in the examined mysteries of the natural world – contained in the details and accumulated truth of great landscapes. The natural history of the landscape was the fundamental discipline of all healthy studies, and the means to personal and social improvement. Catch phrases from *Unto this last* (1860-2) – 'Not greater wealth, but simpler pleasure' – re-echo in *Proserpina*, and relate his broad social vision to the point of view from his desk at Brantwood:

> 'happiness is increased, not by the enlargement of the possessions, but of the heart . . . if thus taught we had . . . the ordering of our house and estate in our own hands, I believe no manner of temperance in pleasure would be better rewarded than that of making our gardens gay only with wild flowers'.

W. J. LINTON, BRANTWOOD AND THE NATURAL HISTORY OF UTOPIA

Ruskin's acquisition of Brantwood arose out of his association with the radical left of British politics. W. J. Linton, the engraver and Republican activist, was an admirer of Ruskin's contributions to utopian democratic propaganda and wrote to his son, from his voluntary exile in the United States in May 1871, that Ruskin might like to buy the house for £1500. 'I would not let anyone else have it so low as I would Ruskin.'

Between March 1852 and April 1855 Linton had written, printed and distributed the paper *The English Republic* very largely from Brantwood. In the post Chartist years, and in the aftermath of the events of 1848 on the continent, Linton's paper was the outstanding voice of radical democracy in England, pressing forward the theoretical arguments for a humane popular government. Linton proposed the sovereignty of a single legislative chamber, elected by universal adult suffrage, but subject to confirmation of its laws by referendum. A leading function of the state was to be the provision of education for all, to cultivate the 'perceptive faculties' of children and to teach the 'broad facts of Nature and God in relation to (their) position in the Universe'. Later, the curriculum would include geology and botany, with gardening as the principal out of school activity.

Linton and Ruskin, for all their differences of temperament and personal morality, shared this Utopian belief in the fundamental utility of natural history to achieve a right sense of the beauty of the world, both present and potential. At Brantwood, Linton and the mother of his children used the woods and hillsides as a schoolroom, and educated their children in some accord with the programme for the Republic.

Linton's flower drawings, including studies for his magnum opus of natural history, *The Ferns of the Lake District* (1864), are very beautiful, and are unpublished though they were given to the Victoria and Albert Museum in 1938 by Kineton Parkes, editor of the journal of the provincial Ruskin societies and custodian into the present century of the Ruskinian Morrisite political heritage. Both in their origin at Brantwood and in their transmission to the present, therefore, they belong to the intellectual history of English radicalism and record the moment of diversification of the socialist and non-socialist traditions from their common ground in Positivist scientific studies.

W. J. LINTON

242 Brantwood 14 July 1867
○ Marsh Cinquefoil, growing
  by the side of a rivulet near
  Hawkshead Cross
  Pencil and watercolour
  20.1 x 16.2 cm.
  Victoria and Albert Museum
  E2777-1938

243 Wood Strawberry Brantwood
  29 May 1865
  Pencil and watercolour
  20.1 x 16.2 cm.
  Victoria and Albert Museum
  E2800-1938

244 Sycamore or Great Maple
  Brantwood 3 May 1865
  Pencil and watercolour
  on one half of a folded sheet
  20.1 x 32.4 cm.
  Victoria and Albert Museum
  E2813-1938

245 Common Prickly Shield Fern
  Growing in the wood above
  Brantwood 30 November 1857
  Pencil and watercolour on one half
  of a folded sheet 20.1 x 32.4 cm.
  Victoria and Albert Museum
  E2784-1938

243

246 Sketchbook open at pp. 2-3
  Blea Tarn and Langdale Pikes
  7 July 1853
  Victoria and Albert Museum
  E2673-1938

247 Sketchbook open at pp. 42-3
○ Wordsworth's Seat Brantwood
  Victoria and Albert Museum
  E2674-1938
The attachment of Wordsworth's name to this viewpoint is interesting, and otherwise unrecorded, but Wordsworth is known to have stayed at Water Park, on Coniston, with his cousin Dorothy Benson Hanison in the 1830's, whose husband owned most of the Furness iron industry.

WINDERMERE

The difference between the first flowering of Arcadian architecture in the Lake District and its later manifestation arose on a point of aesthetic conscience. The question was one of harmony between the building and the landscape, properly apprehended as a construct of its own history and physical character. Could the imposition of the Palladian villa model on a Northern landscape be justified? Were the results successful? Were they the best that could be achieved? The extreme Picturesque preference for concealment led initially to the self effacing single storey house style, but simultaneously Picturesque aesthetics proposed that a more profoundly right answer lay in the simple observation of local style which incorporated the instinctive taste and practical wisdom of those who knew the area best. From the early 1820's Wordsworth's Guide to the Lakes was a powerful advocate of historicism and the vernacular for new building, and of garden design and tree planting which would achieve as harmoniously as possible the integration of new buildings into the existing landscape. George Webster's design for Wordsworth's proposed house at Rydal showed exactly what the master had in mind, but in freer adaptation of the general mood for historicism, wealthy men found other styles.

248

248 Croft Lodge built 1828–30
    Photograph David Lyons 1984

James Brancker, the inheritor of a Liverpool sugar fortune, demolished
an earlier house, one of the Arcadian classical villas of Brathay – 'a neat
white seat on the shores of Windermere'. In this deliberate act of taste,
Brancker built a house which struck everyone as different. Hartley
Coleridge described it as 'a style which neither Vitruvius, Palladio, Inigo
Jones, Piranesi nor Sir Jeffrey Wyatville ever dream'd of, even in a
nightmare, or under the influence of opium'. But Croft's eclecticism
attempted to draw into the landscape at the head of Windermere some
allusions to the English building tradition, from the Renaissance to
Strawberry Hill Gothic, and the castellation acknowledged that Cumbria
within the last century had seen Scottish arms march through it. Under
Loughrigg, against the great sweep of the Rydal fells, it went some
way to match its scale to that of the landscape, and to avoid the charge
of pettiness that increasingly was attached to the pretensions of the
earlier builders.

249 Croft Lodge: the boathouse and the navigable Brathay
    Photograph David Lyons 1984

Brancker was responsible for the changes to the river which Ruskin,
writing to his mother on his honeymoon in 1847, so much deplored. He
continued the festival tradition of boating, and raced yachts against the
neighbouring gentry, but he was at least partly motivated in his schemes
of improvement by the view that, in times of recession, the owner of
capital must spend and incur debt in order to promote employment.

By the 1840's the achievement of a 'historic' style by the use of
castellation and other decorative devices applied superficially to a
conventional Augustan structure seemed inadequate to scholars and
architects. Croft indeed was surprisingly little learned for its date,
especially surprising in a district that had Waterhead House at Coniston
to point the way to a richer and more detailed antiquarianism. The 1840's
however saw easily the most significant attempt to build properly in the
grandest location.

WRAY CASTLE

By H. P. Horner for Dr. James Dawson (1779-1875), a medical doctor of Liverpool who had married money; Wray forms part of the classic views of the head of Windermere, critically sited on a wooded eminence forming a promontory at Watbarrow Point, and providing the unmistakable motif of the view to the Langdale Pikes from the road on the eastern shore of Windermere. Behind it, set back above a system of intricately wooded hills, is the arc of the Coniston Fells, from Wetherlam to the Old Man. More than two generations of the intellectual and artistic élite of Britain had by this time travelled to the Lakes to look at this view of the head of Windermere. It was a staggeringly bold enterprise to place a building, of such innate gestural power, in such a sacred situation.

251

250 Wray Castle
   Photograph by Courtesy of
   Lancashire County Record Office

   RUPERT POTTER
251 Wray Castle 20 August 1899
   Photograph gelatine bromide
   Victoria and Albert Museum Library BP 1319

   BEATRIX POTTER
252 Wray Castle, the Library July 1882
   Watercolour 35.4 x 25.4 cm.
   Victoria and Albert Museum Library BP 231

The views from Wray Castle are of course part of the house's overall rhetoric. The woodland pressing quite closely on the lawns and terraces and allowing glimpses across the Lake to the Troutbeck and Ambleside fells, was evidently carefully preserved and interplanted when the house was built in order to encourage the historical illusionism. The interior, both architecturally and in its furnishings, had much of the lavish eclecticism associated with the Great Exhibition style, but in that was equally part of the address to the inhabitants' sense of themselves as inheritors of a significant past. Wray, in the photographs taken by Rupert Potter of his family as tenants of the house, was clearly comfortable in that profounder way of providing right spaces to inhabit and move through, and exciting in the close-up drama of its top heavy towers rearing over terraces ornamented with ruins. But Wray must always have been primarily a house to be looked at, seen from the classic distances that allowed its scale a proper relation to the landscape around it. In that context of immemorial hills, it was a prompt to the active imagination to reflect on the great issues of transience – of war and peace, of stress and security, the whole process that connects the present with the past.

BELSFIELD, BOWNESS

253 Belsfield c.1840 with later extensions
      Photograph David Lyons 1984

Contemporary with Wray Castle, and a similarly bold addition to the pastoral eastern shore of Windermere with its intricately balanced system of Arcadian villas dating from the 1780's and 1790's, was Belsfield, a house attributed to Wordsworth's architect George Webster. It was begun about 1840 for the Baroness de Sternberg, and grew massively in successive extensions both for the Sternbergs and for their successor the industrialist H. W. Schneider after 1869. The extensions altered the originally vertical emphasis of the composition, graced by its tower, which must have represented a conscious attempt to punctuate the slope above the Bowness waterfront with a suitably prominent structure. The design, which is uncompromisingly Italianate, echoed the prevailing Arcadian classical idiom of the central reaches of the lake, and the garden, with its lawns and minimal shrubberies, thus contributed to the effect inaugurated by Thomas White at Belle Isle sixty years earlier.

253

Wordsworth had written, 'should an aversion to old fashions unfortunately exist, accompanied with a desire to transplant into the cold and stormy North, the elegancies of a villa formed upon a model taken from countries with a milder climate' – the house should be deeply embowered in trees and should 'scarcely be seen'.

Belsfield never had that sort of Picturesque treatment, though other houses, in the Italianate villa style of the second quarter of the century, notably The Craig (demolished), built for Lord Decies c. 1837, and The Knoll, for Harriet Martineau, certainly did.

THE KNOLL

254 The Knoll Ambleside
    Photograph Francis Frith Series no. 3969
    Victoria and Albert Museum

Built for Harriet Martineau in the winter of 1845-6. The Italianate villa, especially on this reduced scale, may be seen as one of the characteristic and brilliant inventions of mid–nineteenth century bourgeois domestic architecture, especially associated with the houses of married dons in Oxford and Cambridge, and with certain London suburbs in the expanding ring of the 1840's. In the Lake District it marked the adaptation of the Arcadian tradition to the physical needs and cultural consciousness of the wider middle class market – a process analogous to that of Harriet Martineau's own intellectual work. An image of her house engraved for the title page of her Guide to the Lakes signifies accurately the contents of her book, which, among Lake District Guides, is surely remarkable for the degree of its concentration on the populated as opposed to the 'natural' landscape. Martineau's great strength as a commentator lies in her vivid sociological grasp of the landscape as a living, peopled object of aesthetic pleasure, and there is no hint of lament for the changed landscape as she stands on the terrace at Elleray and catalogues the new houses with the relish of an estate agent:

254

'All below are woods, with houses peeping out; on a height of the opposite shore, Wray Castle; further north, the little Brathay Chapel ... the little white houses of Clappersgate, with the chateau-like mansion of Croft Lodge conspicuous above the rest ... The village of Windermere is like nothing that is to be seen anywhere else. The new buildings (and all are new) are of the dark grey stone of the region, and are for the most part of a medieval style of architecture. The Reverend J. A. Addison, late of Windermere, had a passion for ecclesiastical architecture; and his example has been a good deal followed. There is the little church of St. Mary, and there are the schools belonging to it, with their steep roofs of curiously shaped slates: and there is St. Mary's Abbey ... and St. Mary's Cottage. And there is the new college of St. Mary, standing in a fine position, between the main road and the descent to the lake ... The large house, on the hill and amidst the woods of the Elleray estate ... is (Oakland) the property of John Gandy, Esq., who has chosen a charming site for his abode: and a little further, on the same side of the road, is the pretty villa-residence (The Wood) of Miss Yates.'

'There is a new house, built just below the ridge at Miller Brow by William Sheldon (Highfield), which we have thought, from the time the foundation was laid, the most enviable abode in the country ... Cook's House has only just disappeared, and a new residence, built by Peter Kennedy Esq. (Cook's Hall), has taken its place. There are villas on either side of the road, on almost every favourable spot, all the way to Bowness ... We pass rows of lodging houses ... Further on is the Hydropathic Establishment, conducted by Mr. E. L. Hudson, F.R.C.S.'

HARRIET MARTINEAU 1802-76
255 A Complete Guide to the English Lakes
    Windermere and London 1855, five editions to 1876
    King's College Cambridge Bicknell Collection
The Guide first appeared in this form as a quarto volume with four colour plates, six outlines of mountains, and in some copies with six engravings after Aspland and Pettit. It was republished in the year of its appearance as an octavo, a more pocketable format. Both versions contained 'A Map Coloured Geologically by John Ruthven'.

THE RAILWAY AT WINDERMERE

The great change that had come about in the view, at least southward from Elleray and Orrest Head, was the arrival of the railway in 1847. It was one of a number of developments realised at about this time, including the Lancaster Carlisle line of 1846, and the Cockermouth Workington, also of 1847. Shares of the proposed Windermere branch of the line from Oxenholme via Kendal were advertised in the *Westmorland Gazette* of 31 August 1844 and were fully subscribed within a week. A month later a committee of landowners and 'others whose interest may be affected' was set up under the chairmanship of Professor Wilson of Elleray. The published plan of the Railway Company that the line should reach to Low Wood clearly impinged on the estates of those, like Wilson, his neighbour Lord Bradford, Messrs. Dunlop and Benson, whose villas would be cut off from the lake, their view interrupted by viaducts, and their withdrawn calm disturbed. On the 19 October Wordsworth's name was added to the list. Sensing the imminence of defeat, the company announced tactically that the line would terminate south of Orrest Head, at the hamlet of Birthwaite.

Wordsworth, with no personal or financial axe to grind, pursued his disinterested opposition and wrote to the *Morning Post* for 9 December 1844. Lines already under construction would bring passengers to Penrith, four miles from Ullswater, and to Oxenholme, nine miles from Windermere. This was enough, he argued, and the transportation of large numbers of people into the heart of the Lake District would in any case destroy the amenity they came to enjoy.

The company replied that although there would be crowds around the terminus, the rest of the district would be unaffected, and would 'retain its character of retirement and seclusion'. The line was accordingly built, and was opened in April 1847. The Birthwaite Terminus – 'Windermere Station' – and the new Windermere Hotel, marked the foundation of the new town, Windermere, which grew up around the railhead and extended itself more or less continuously down the road to Bowness. William Cockin's image of a town on the lake in emulation of Geneva was thus in some measure fulfilled.

Having beaten off the proposal to push the line as far north as Low Wood, the gentry of the Windermere littoral learnt to live with the railway and its tourists. Property prices rose, floating up in the general economic boom of the 1850's. Professor Wilson died and Elleray was bought in 1855 by William Eastted who tidied up the estate, laid out new drives in the grounds, and opened new viewpoints to the public in exchange for contributions to the new Church and school of St. Mary's at the foot of the hill by the roadside.

At this time the social preponderance of Windermere over Bowness, on the crude but dramatic measure of identifiable gentry listed in Harriet Martineau's *Directory*, was clear. Windermere had at least forty two household heads listed as either Reverend or Esq., or with some clear female status indicator. Bowness, far stronger in tradespeople, had nine. There was certainly a tendency to list houses which physically seem part of Bowness in the Windermere section – for example William Greg renting The Craig, Admiral Sir Thomas Pasley at Craig Foot and the Reverend Thomas Staniforth at Storrs, all appear for Windermere, but if this indicates a preference, it reinforces the point. Apart from the old established Curwens at Belle Isle and George Marwood who was still at Old England, few of the other listed gentry are at addresses of much status. Bowness was already a tourist town, with no less than sixteen households, hotels or lodging houses, explicitly dependent on the passing trade. In 1869 Marwood's house was pulled down and the first (central) section of the Hotel was put up by Thomas Pattinson, in what was now emerging as the local, 'house style' of the firm.

JAMES BAKER PYNE 1800–70
256 Windermere from Orrest Head
O Lithograph 53.3 x 66 cm.
separated from the series
The English Lake District
Trustees of Dove Cottage

WILLIAM WORDSWORTH 1770–1850
257 Manuscript draft of letter to the
Editor of the *Morning Post*
published 9 December 1844
expressing reasoned opposition to
the construction of the Oxenholme
Kendal Windermere branch railway
Trustees of Dove Cottage

258 Proof of printed letter to the Editor
of the *Morning Post*, including the
sonnet 'Is there no nook of English
ground secure', corrected in
manuscript by Wordsworth and his
son-in-law Edward Quillinan
Trustees of Dove Cottage

259 Bradshaw's Guide, The Lakes . . .
with a Map of the Lake District
Time Tables of the Railway
Steamers and Coaches and a List
of Excursions
Manchester and London 1848
King's College Cambridge
Bicknell Collection

260 Rigg's Windermere Hotel
Photograph
David Lyons 1984
The architect was Miles Thompson of
Kendal, the builder Abraham Pattinson,
and the first proprietor Richard Rigg. It
was opened in time for the tourist season
on 12 May 1847.

261 New building at Windermere
Photograph
Francis Frith
Series no. 3600
Victoria and Albert Museum

264

266

REVEREND WILLIAM FORD
270 A Description of the Scenery of the
    Lake District
    Carlisle 1839
    seventh edition 1852
    King's College Cambridge
    Bicknell Collection
Leigh's and Ford's guides are typical
pocket guides of the second quarter of
the century, similar in format and in
their expectation of the interests of their
readers. They have clear maps to
encourage modest exploration, and
acknowledge gratefully the influence
of Wordsworth.

THOMAS ROSE
271 Westmorland, Cumberland
    Durham and Northumberland
    London 1832
    Issued in parts in printed paper
    wrappers as part of Fisher's
    *Picturesque Illustrations of Great
    Britain and Ireland*, 213 steel
    engravings from drawings by
    Allom, Gastineau and Pickering by
    various engravers
    Trustees of Dove Cottage
Prints from these fine and durable steel
plates were produced in large numbers
for many years. They were used in
various books and for a variety of
purposes such as headings for letter
paper and for table mats.

272 Writing paper headed with
    impressions of the plates from
    Rose's *Westmorland and Cumberland*
    Peter Bicknell

273 Views of the English Lakes on
    writing paper
    Sold in a blue printed envelope
    engraved by Banks and Co.
    Edinburgh
    Trustees of Dove Cottage

274 Black's Guide to the Lakes
    Edinburgh 1856
    King's College Cambridge

Bicknell Collection
Black's Shilling Guide, an
abbreviated version of Black's
Picturesque Guide
open at p. 7 to show advertisement
for Birket Foster's Views

MYLES BIRKET FOSTER 1825-99
275 Views of the English Lakes
    Edinburgh
    n.d. (1856)
    King's College Cambridge
    Bicknell Collection
    24 engravings by E. Evans after
    Birket Foster; apparently a separate
    publication of the illustrations to
    Black's Picturesque Guide.

T. L. ASPLAND 1807-89
276 Views of the English Lakes
    and Mountains
    London and Windermere
    (Garnett) n.d.
    8 views, coloured by Aspland
    with a pamphlet, packed in a
    small portfolio
    King's College Cambridge
    Bicknell Collection

277 At Windermere 1849
    Watercolour, gouache
    41.3 x 54 cm.

(oval)

Apland's elaborate neo-pastoral images were advertised in Martineau's Guide. He was, with Petit, one of the most successful local suppliers of 'original' (as opposed to printed) views of the Lakes. This is a relatively early and distinctly magnificent example.

278 Our English Lakes Mountains
 and Waterfalls
 London 1864
 Mounted photographic prints
 anonymous
 King's College Cambridge
 Bicknell Collection
The first Lake District book to be illustrated with photographs.

JAMES PAYN
279 The English Lakes
 One Shilling Guide
 Windermere
 (Garnett) n.d.
 Fourth edition
 c.1865
 King's College Cambridge
 Bicknell Collection
Garnett of Windermere was one of the principal purveyors of maps, guides, prints and miscellaneous tourist items to visitors.

280 Garnett's Travelling Maps of the
 Lake District
 London and Windermere
 (Garnett) n.d.
 (c.1865)
 King's College Cambridge
 Bicknell Collection

281 Jenkinson's Practical Guide to the
 English Lakes
 London 1873-6
 King's College Cambridge
 Bicknell Collection
In four separate sections, a map in each.

280

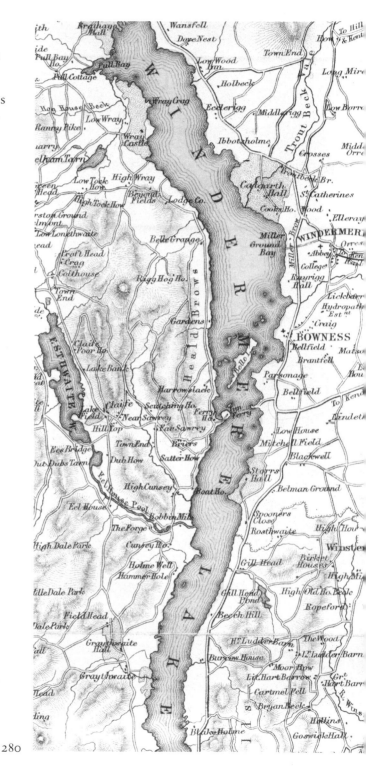

The fate of the original lakeside villa at Old England was not typical. The tourist boom led to the building of such vast new hotels usually on green field sites, as with Bownass' Ullswater Hotel at Patterdale or the Prince of Wales at Grasmere, or by the expansion of traditional coaching inns like the Low Wood or the Red Lion at Grasmere. In a development of some symbolic interest, villas built by a previous generation for private residence or letting were converted into hotels. Both economy and the borrowed prestige of the former owner's life-style or name made conversion advantageous. Thus in Grasmere, Moss Head House, built in 1871-2 for the Earl of Cadogan, lasted only ten years as a private house before the iron laws of trade caused its conversion into the Rothay Hotel. R. Hudson the proprietor, emphasised the facilities for gentry sports – croquet, archery and bowls on the lawn, and in the conservatory the availability of exotic fruit. But the process was not simple nor one way. Hotels like The Hollens reverted to private houses in the mid-century, and in no sense were the hotels less the playground of the rich or titled. Both villas and hotels were contemporary phenomena of the bourgeois landscape culture in the later nineteenth century, and the pricing policy of the great hoteliers, together with the state visits by queens, princes and kaisers, ensured that the distinction between house and hotel was not one of relative expense nor of old as against new money.

Along the eastern shore of Windermere the daisy chain of dream houses grew – the new Elleray, with a tower in the Italianizing manner as at Belsfield, built in 1869 for Mr. A. H. Heywood (1826-1901) on the site of Professor Wilson's single storey house; Holehird (1869) in a steep gabled idiom for Mr. J. M. Dunlop (d. 1878), the Priory in flamboyant Gothic for the Carver family, also in 1869; Browhead for Mr. Edward Cohen, finished c. 1873, and Chapel Ridding for Mr. Gibson (1808-1897), whose garden was laid out with special care. The northern push out of Windermere established by the 1880's a colony of some of the richest and, as far as consciousness of landscape amenity was concerned, the most determined householders in the country. When, in 1887, the proposal to extend the railway to Ambleside was revived, the owners of the houses affected, mostly those highest on the slopes above Windermere, formed themselves into a lobby to defeat the bill in Parliament.

Robert Dunlop of Holehird petitioned individually, on the grounds that a fifty foot high embankment was planned to run below his house, severing his drive and cutting off the entrance lodge. He went on: 'Property in the district of Windermere Lake is all but worthless if the views of the lake and surrounding country are interfered with. The views from your Petitioner's residence and estate generally will, by the proposed embankment and roadway, be interfered with very materially, the views of the lake and mountains from the residence being practically shut out by the said embankment.'

Other owners submitted a collective petition, objecting in similar terms to the compulsory purchase powers in the bill: Frances Turrill, the new owner of Browhead pointing out that the line would pass along the steep bank directly above the entrance to the house on which a special

189

195

197

204

227

235

Brantwood by JK?
before additions

Marsh Cinquefoil
(Comarum palustre),

Perennial.
(Growing by the side of a
rivulet near Hawks-
head Cross).

Brantwood
July 14, 1867.

E.2777-1938

242

247

256

307

343

344

CITY OF MANCHESTER.

THIRLMERE WATERWORKS.

The above sketch represents the appearance of the Lake when raised to the statutory limit of height of 50 feet.

City of Manchester.

THIRLMERE WATERWORKS.

THE WATER FOR THE SUPPLY TO THE CITY OF MANCHESTER AND DISTRICT WILL
BE IMPOUNDED BY MEANS OF MASONRY EMBANKMENTS
AT THE NORTH END OF LAKE THIRLMERE, NEAR BRIDGE END FARM.

The Length of the Lake, when raised 50 feet, will be	3¾ Miles 220 Yards
Area of the Lake	793 Statute Acres
Holding Capacity of the Lake	8,135,000,000 Gallons
Elevation above Ordnance Datum	583 Feet
Total Drainage Ground (the whole of which is the property of the Corporation of Manchester)	11,000 Acres
Length of Embankment	286 Yards

AQUEDUCT WORKS.

Diameter of Straining Well at Wythburn, for the admission of Water into the Aqueduct from the Lake	37 Feet 6 Inches
Total Length of Aqueduct from Thirlmere to Manchester	95 Miles
Which includes:—	
Tunnels	13½ Miles
Cut and Cover	37½ ,,
Pipes	44 ,,
Diameter of Aqueduct	7 feet
Diameter of Main Pipes	48, 40, and 36 Inches
Fall of Aqueduct per Mile	20 Inches
Estimated Daily Supply of Water, in addition to Compensation	50,000,000 Gallons

INSCRIPTION ON THE STONE TO BE FIXED ON EMBANKMENT.

MANCHESTER CORPORATION WATERWORKS.

THIRLMERE.

THE FIRST STONE OF THIS EMBANKMENT WAS LAID ON THE 22nd AUGUST, 1890, by

ALDERMAN SIR JOHN JAMES HARWOOD, KNIGHT.

Alderman JOHN MARK, Mayor.

WATERWORKS COMMITTEE
Alderman Sir John James Harwood, Knight, *Chairman.*
Councillor Bosdin Thomas Leech, *Deputy-Chairman.*

ALDERMEN
Joseph Lamb,   Hugo Shaw,   Walton Smith,   Joseph Thompson.

COUNCILLORS
John Harris Andrews,   Joseph Brooks,   Robert Gibson,   William Telford Gunson,
John Hinchliffe, James Hoy, Abraham Evans Lloyd, Alexander McDougall, Junr.,
Henry Charles Pingstone, John Roberts, Samuel Barton Worthington.

GEORGE HENRY HILL, *Engineer.*   WILLIAM HENRY TALBOT, *Town Clerk.*

THIRLMERE WATERWORKS.

CONCILIO ET LABORE

360

363

385

389

394

398

garden of evergreens was laid out; Edward Gibson at Chapel Ridding was also set to lose his garden, and John Bore and William Lister, joint Trustees of Dove Nest, pointed out that the estate 'celebrated in the district for the beauty of its situation and surroundings' would be split along its length, two houses and a cottage on the land ruined by the line within sixty yards of them. The hardest case was that of John Rigg, proprietor and manager of the Windermere Hotel. The proposal there was to pass the line in a shallow tunnel through the front garden of the hotel, ten yards from the door and underneath the coach houses: Rigg pointed out that the 'annoyance and discomfort' of trains passing so close would ruin his business.

The Petitioners carried their point, and the Bill fell. Had the line been built it would now be valued as the most stunningly ambitious example of engineering and landscape architecture, perhaps comparable with Brunel's Cornwall line, or the Carlisle and Settle. The ironies of history are such that a proposal now to close the line would challenge the capacity of a modern lobby to carry its point in Parliament.

285

282 The Ullswater Hotel Patterdale
Photograph Francis Frith series
Victoria and Albert Museum

283 Prince of Wales Hotel Grasmere
Photograph Francis Frith
series 1676
Victoria and Albert Museum

284 Elleray 1869
Photograph
David Lyons 1984

RUPERT POTTER
285 Holehird Windermere
August 1889
Photograph albumen
Victoria and Albert Library
BP 1331

286 The Priory 1869
Photograph
David Lyons 1984

287 Browhead c.1873
Photograph
David Lyons 1984

288 Chappel Ridding 1873
Photograph
David Lyons 1984

289 Plan of proposed extension of railway from Windermere
    to Ambleside

290 Detail showing line of railway through the frontage of
    Windermere Hotel
    Photograph
    Trustees of Dove Cottage by courtesy of Fisher Hoggarth Kendal

291 The Craig Estate c. 1960
    Photograph David Lyons 1984

292 The Greenbank Estate Ambleside
    Photograph David Lyons 1984

289

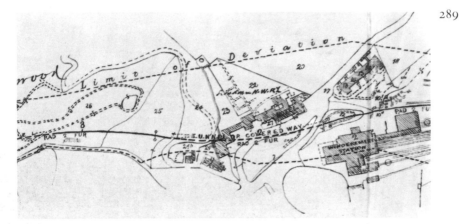

Of that group of houses which survived the 1887 railway work,
Browhead, and Chapel Ridding together wth Elleray, now make up the
campus of a girls' boarding school: the millionaire view along the length
of Windermere to the peaks of Langdale now spreads sweetness and light
amongst the daughters of the northern bourgeoisie. Towards Bowness,
The Craig, which had become a boys' preparatory school soon after the
First World War, and from which at midsummer midnight a party of
boys would set out to watch the sun rise from the top of Helvellyn, was
sold by its proprietor and headmaster as a housing estate. Instead of
children, elderly freeholders lift up their eyes to the hills. The anxiety,
the pressing question, which faced developers in the second quarter of
the nineteenth century about building to enhance the landscape and in
harmony with its architectural and natural history, had passed by 1960 to
the official planners. It is interesting that the modern custodians of taste
turned back in this case to the Pricean resort of the 'bungalow', as though
it were wise to intrude on the eye as little as possible, to hug the ground
with light nut shell structures. But they created on this estate a
convoluted lay out that actually seems to turn inward towards the
minute circle of garden and garage walk, away from the majestic view.

   The modest, tentative quality of the building at The Craig, bizarrely
symbolized in preserved relics of its former gardens, technically accords

with the conservationist principles of the historic Picturesque. In contrast, perhaps, the Greenbank estate at Ambleside sweeps boldly up the fell side on the south bank of the Scandale beck, arranged in great sweeping curves with the odd isolated tree arising out of smoothed turf and mown lawns: a culverted beck follows the serpentine line of the main access road.

Aesthetically the estate seems to look back to the classicising idiom so well entrenched at this northern end of Windermere at Rydal Hall, Brathay Hall and nearby at Belmount: self-confident public enterprise, more certain of the virtue of housing those qualified from the list, manages the green field site with radical panache. There is not the slightest attempt at creating or imposing 'community', no hint of the village, or of planting for enriched close-up effects. Each house commands a view across the Rothay valley to the shoulder of Loughrigg, and has its share of the lawns and serpentine beck; each house, and the estate in general, is a presence in the landscape: neo-classical, neo-Whig in its imagery of harmonious individualism.

291

BEATRIX POTTER

Helen Beatrix Potter was born 28 July 1866 in London, at 2 Bolton Gardens. Her father, Rupert Potter, was second generation money, his father Edmund having been a calico printer in Glossop, the chief town of the Derbyshire textile industry. Edmund rode the boom in manufacturing of the 1850's and 1860's so successfully that the family was, by the time of Beatrix Potter's birth, very wealthy. Edmund retired from business, Rupert became (nominally) a barrister, and the Potters came south. Beatrix's earliest and happiest memories were of her grandfather's house at Camfield Place in Hertfordshire: 'the notes of the stable clock and the all pervading smell of new mown hay, the distant

295

sounds of the farmyard, the feeling of plenty, well-assured, indolent wealth, honourably earned and wisely spent, charity without ostentation, opulence without pride...'

In London on the other hand, the sober routine of the Kensington bourgeoisie seemed overwhelming. Rupert Potter led his life around his clubs and Mrs Potter supervised the domestic staff, paying and receiving calls from her acquaintances in the afternoon. In this routine, the annual holiday was, as Ruskin, a similarly privileged and isolated London child, described it, a time of eye opening wonder. For much of Beatrix Potter's childhood the family went to Perthshire. For the summer of 1882, when she was sixteen, they rented Wray Castle on Windermere for the first time.

293 RUPERT POTTER
    Wray Castle with the Potter family August 1882
    Photograph gelatine bromide
    Victoria and Albert Museum Library BP 1320 (b)
Beatrix is in the middle, Bertram her brother on the left, with Mr. and Mrs. Potter on the right: the shutter was evidently worked by time-elapse or was pressed by a servant.

293

RUPERT POTTER   Rupert Potter is a significant English landscape photographer of the golden age, still barely distinguished by the photo historians, but now emerging as a figure in his own right, mainly on the basis of prints in the Beatrix Potter archive in the Victoria and Albert Museum Library, of a previously unknown group recently given to the Department of Photographs, and of an album in the possession of Frederick Warne and Company. He seems to have worked largely on holiday; in Scotland his work was done in some sort of collaboration with his friend Millais, who used prints by him in the painting of his photo based landscapes of the 1870's and after. The quasi-Realistic aesthetics of Pre-Raphaelitism presumably underpin Potter's markedly non pictorial approach to his art. There is no straining after a painterly effect in subject, composition or visual texture; the images, isolating moments and parts of places from the stream of observation, are specifically and necessarily photographic.

294 Beatrix, Rupert and Bertram
     October 1881
     Photograph gelatine bromide
     Victoria and Albert Museum
     Library

295 Bertram, Rupert and Beatrix
     October 6 1902
     Photograph gelatine bromide
     Victoria and Albert Museum
     Library

296 Fawe Park Interior 1903
     Photograph gelatine bromide
     Victoria and Albert Museum
     Library BP 1358

297 Lingholm 2 August 1897
     Photograph gelatine bromide
     Victoria and Albert Museum
     Library BP 1538

298 Lingholm 1 August 1898
     Photograph gelatine bromide
     Victoria and Albert Museum
     Library BP 1535

299 Derwentwater from Fawe Park
     September 1903
     Photograph gelatine bromide
     Victoria and Albert Museum
     Library BP 1357

296

29

Between 1885 and 1903, no less than six summers were spent near
Derwentwater, usually at Ling Holme, and once at Fawe Park (in 1903),
two important houses by Waterhouse, in equally important garden
settings, on the western shore of the lake. In 1889 the Potters took
Holehird on Windermere, in 1896 Lakefield, a house with grounds
stretching down to the shores of Esthwaite. When one thinks of the way
in which the great villas of the Lake District – such deliberate additions to
the landscape – were used in the high minded consciousness that 'Nature
has set aside her Sublime bits for us to think and feel in', one can do no
better than imagine the Potters arriving from Kensington in the train;
seeking relief, tranquillity and moral stimulus in the rich historicising
interiors, the gardens and the immemorial hills.

Beatrix's use of landscape was different from, and of course of infinitely
greater celebrity than, that of her father. Her wonderful animal fantasy

books after *Peter Rabbit* derive more or less closely from responses to the landscape round Derwentwater and Esthwaite, and from the interiors of houses with which she was personally connected. There seems to have been an element of reaction against the decorous Arcadianism of her family holidays, and her personal style must be associated with the emergence in the wider world of the architecture and aesthetics of idealized rural domesticity of the Ernest Gimson-Sidney Barnsley school in the late 1890's. Thus her acquisition of Hill Top, a working farm at Sawrey, in 1905 was an act of independence in her family life, and it was also a declaration of aesthetic commitment – of preference for the cottage rather than the house – which soon bore fruit in illustrations for *Mrs. Tiggy-Winkle* and *The Tale of the Pie and the Patty Pan.* The images of Mrs Tiggy-Winkle's kitchen, the stools, chests, high shelves and dressers.

300

propose a manner of life, cosy and reassuring, which is of the essence of the Gimson–Barnsley aesthetic, and which is of fundamental importance in the whole address that the book makes to the mind of a child. At the slightly higher social level of the *Pie and the Patty Pan,* Ribby and the Duchess, a cat and a dog, take tea amid scenes based closely on studies make in Sawrey, in Hill Top itself and in the Lakefield cottages. The book, a warm hearted comedy of manners, is like all Beatrix Potter's work, profoundly moral and educative.

There is necessarily, in order to make the warmth and security of the hearth doubly evident, a tendency to represent the outside world as threatening, sometimes overtly so, sometimes only relatively. Adventurism, the readiness of characters to go outside the safety of home, exposes them to dangers. Jemima Puddle-Duck, who abandons the farmyard with some very rightous indignation for the apparently idyllic hillside and woodland above Esthwaite, finds the fox – all sinister masculine politeness and ambiguity – who invites her to use his 'holiday villa'. There is not much benignity nor immanent harmony in the Nature encountered by Jemima, and the dog who saves her is a familiar, perhaps even parental figure from the Hill Top farmyard.

Tom Kitten has the most horrifying experience of all, lost and trussed up in the mysterious inner places of Hill Top, as his mother wanders mewing along the landings and corridors. Hill Top, by the date of *Samuel Whiskers,* was a highly sophisticated excerise in contemporary design. Based on drawings of what she had already achieved in constructing an ideal home for herself, the images against which the threatened kitten is shown, are powerfully normative, intended to discourage straying.

The basic perception that the outside world is dangerous and the inner world of hearth and home is safe, goes back far as an influence in the history of landscape, architecture and garden design, and was particularly relevant historically in the response to mountains as images of terror. Other writers, responding to the same landscape as Beatrix Potter, and with the same basic perception of the danger/security pairing, proposed a different morality. The point is made with surprising directness in the first pages of Arthur Ransome's *Swallows and Amazons* (1930), when the telegram from Daddy – whose ship was at Malta but

303

Plate from Swallows and Amazons

136

under orders for Hong Kong – permits a possibly dangerous sailing expedition for the children with the words 'BETTER DROWNED THAN DUFFERS IF NOT DUFFERS WON'T DROWN.' The story that follows is a triumphant assertion of the virtue of the outdoor, its capacity to provide the critical lessons of growing up, to provide a context in which self-reliance and group-reliance are seen as essential and fun, and in which a little danger, with some discreet supervision and a lot of individual sense, is nothing but a good thing.

One should not labour these points, which are made with the success that comes from subtlety in the books, but clearly the doctrine of children's literature such as this leads on to other forms of self testing and challenge seeking in the landscape, to rock climbing, sailing and so on. It makes up what has been for the twentieth century perhaps the dominant mode of response to the landscape.

Illustrations 300 to 303
© Reproduced by kind permission of
Frederick Warne and Company Limited

300 BEATRIX POTTER
Mrs. Tiggy-Winkle 1901-5
Pencil and watercolour
21.2 x 17.9 cm.
Victoria and Albert Museum
Library BP 499

301 Tabitha Twitchit, duplicate
○ illustration for *The Tale of Samuel Whiskers* 1906-8
Watercolour
24 x 20 cm.
Victoria and Albert Museum
Library BP 509

302 Setting for *The Pie and the Patty Pan* 1903-5; the door of Sawrey Post Office
Pencil and watercolour
19.7 x 22.8 cm.
Victoria and Albert Museum
Library BP 502

303 Table mat, with autograph repetition of illustration to the *Tale of Jemima Puddle-Duck* 1908
'She set off on a fine spring afternoon along the cartroad that leads over the hill. She was wearing a shawl and poke bonnet'
Watercolour, gouache on silk circular, diameter 10.2 cm.
Victoria and Albert Museum
Library

LATER PAINTERS

The first 'revolution' against classical formalism in landscape dates as we have seen from the 1790's: the second from roughly the moment at Fontainebleau when Ruskin, according to his own account, realised the triumphant fact of Nature's superiority and the excellence of the random in matters of composition. The Romantics, with their partly psychological commitment to originality as a guiding principle of art and their interest in empirical observational science, developed a visual aesthetic of close-up sketch like picture making. On this basis and with the reinforcement of Ruskin's doctrine, the landscape realists of the mid century emerged, in close association with the painters of the Pre-Raphaelite Brotherhood. Pictures produced within this aesthetic were certainly not sketchy in technique, but were similarly meant to be painted in front of the subject. They were highly finished and detailed assemblages of objects, usually bright coloured and filling the frame with an evenly distributed focus from the centre to the periphery. The best examples here are those by Atkinson Grimshaw and Daniel Alexander Williamson, who illustrate simultaneously that within the Ruskinian-Realist aesthetic, painting tended as strongly towards the condition of photography as photography did initially towards painting.

Williamson also reminds us that, with the implementation of a public policy to set up art schools throughout the country from the 1840's, specifically intended to broaden the aesthetic and imaginative horizons of the artisan-designer class, there was an upsurge in creativity in the provinces. The young men and women emerging from the National Schools, headquartered at South Kensington, began to come on stream in the 1850's, at the inspirational moment of the Ruskinian aesthetic, with the result that the school of landscape painting that we sometimes call Pre-Raphaelite is, unlike most major movement in art history, extraordinarily widespread and carried on by artists whose names often mean little. Williamson, to a metropolitan audience (though emphatically not in Liverpool), may seem to be one of these, an extraordinarily gifted painter with a largely local reputation, but G. H. Newton is much more lost to history. His *Jack's Craig* was purchased by the Victoria and Albert Museum in 1863 as one of an extremely interesting group of eight pictures by 'Art Masters' – the teachers in the National Schools. Newton was the master of the Durham School of Art from its opening in May 1853, at least until 1871. His oeuvre, stylistically a homage to Richard Redgrave at South Kensington, was largely made up of Lake District subjects and prompts the thought that the rise of the

National Schools helped the North to recover control of the Lake District landscape in a pictorial sense as it was later to do in matters of access and administration. The same tendency is evident in the fact that, whereas the collections of the national museums are strongest in the art of the Lake District up to about 1850, from then on easily the best pictures are in Liverpool and Manchester. The gathering commitment of Manchester people to the Lakes in the twentieth century – indeed their daily baptism in its waters – is benignly symbolised in the riches of the City's Art Gallery, which charts the evolution of the pictorial tradition in the Lake District through both the neo-romantic and the abstractionist tendencies of the century's art.

It is perhaps a mistake to trace a consistent movement away from the classically formalised picture making of the eighteenth century to the abstract, conceptual and event-oriented work of the mid twentieth century: in a simple sense the movement was there, but just as Constable in 1806 found the profoundest lessons in the eloquence and spatial elegance of the classic Lake District views, so did Paul Nash, who

310

similarly longed to discover a pictorial rhetoric commensurate with his sense of meanings in landscape. The rigorous spatial organisation and the puritanical linearism of Ben Nicholson and the young contemporary Jon Groom gains in communicative power from analogies with the neo-classical draughtsmen – perhaps here Francis Towne. In a Romantic tradition, Kurt Schwitters' construction of the third *Merzbau* from the unregarded rubbish of society, recalls Dorothy Wordsworth's collection of anecdote – 'Matthew Jobson's lost a cow. Tom Nichol has two good horses strayed' – as the material of her brother's poetry. And in the Ruskinian tradition, perhaps the crystalline momentary nature of the artefacts recorded in the Andy Goldsworthy photographs looks back to the instantaneous 'photographic' imagery of the Pre-Raphaelite landscape. The image of the icicle piercing the rock gains enormously from consciousness of the nineteenth century debate on glaciation: the triumph of the ice over the rock becomes a warning as peremptory as Ruskin's 'dreadful Hammers', that the landscape proposes gods and observances different from those of the Bible and Prayer Book.

The late Ruskinian sense of the world in flux, the mystic movements of materials from place to place, rising and falling in strata that record the age of the earthly creation, perhaps also lies behind the simple re-enactment by David Nash of a stream in Grizedale. What these artists themselves mean is perhaps less important than the fact that they join a continuity of discourse and that their language is inescapably made up of accumulated usages and layered ambiguities, especially rich in an address to a subject like the Lake District which has been a key presence in the consciousness of a whole people for some two and a half centuries.

305

JOHN HARPER 1809-42
304 In Yewdale near Coniston
    28 August 1840
    Watercolour 18.4 x 27.2 cm.
    Victoria and Albert Museum
    E116-1935
The continuity between the optical naturalism of the romantic sketch and the sort of work promoted by the teachers of drawing in the second quarter of the century, is evident here. Ruskin himself was taught by J. D. Harding, and presumably Harper, had he lived beyond the year in which Ruskin had his moment of conversion to 'natural composition' on the road at Fontainebleau, would have evolved in the same direction.

WILLIAM JAMES BLACKLOCK
1815?-58
305 Catbells and Causey Pike 1854
    Oil on canvas 32.7 x 55.9 cm.
    Carlisle Museum and Art Gallery

ROBERT TONGE 1823-56
306 Silver Rock Grasmere
    Oil on canvas
    105.5 x 156 cm.
    Birkenhead Williamson Art Gallery

DANIEL ALEXANDER WILLIAMSON
1823-1903
307 Spring; Arnside Knott and Coniston
○   Range of Hills from Warton Crag
    Oil on canvas 27 x 40.7 cm.
    Liverpool Walker Art Gallery

308 Near the Duddon
    Oil on canvas 44 x 58.7 cm.
    Birkenhead Williamson Art Gallery

ALFRED WILLIAM HUNT 1830-96
309 Stybarrow Crag Ullswater
    Oil on canvas 38 x 60.3 cm.
    Liverpool Walker Art Gallery

ATKINSON GRIMSHAW 1836-93
310 Nab Scar
    Oil on canvas
    Christopher Wood Gallery

GEORGE H. NEWTON fl. 1858-71
311 Jack's Craig Borrowdale 1860
    Oil on canvas 32.7 x 47.4 cm.
    Victoria and Albert Museum
    9147-1863

HENRY HOLIDAY 1839-1927
312 View across Coniston from
    Brantwood c. 1880-90
    Oil on panel 14.7 x 23.5 cm.
    Abbot Hall Art Gallery Kendal

PAUL NASH 1889-1946
313 Thirlmere 1914
○   Pastel and watercolour
    35.6 x 37.5 cm.
    Birmingham Museum and
    Art Gallery
Nash went to the Lake District with his
future wife in the summer of 1914 to
stay with his friend the playwright
Gordon Bottomley at Silverdale in
Lancashire, across the sands from the
Lakes. The landscape was something of
a revelation to him; with its clear classic
lay out on the grand scale it showed him
a way forward from the densely worked
vertical studies of trees of the preceding
years. 'The really big design of this

particular part of the country is
exhilirating' he told Bottomley; and to
John Rothenstein he wrote: 'I saw a new
country quite different to mine – boney
and stark at places and infinitely varied'.

SIR CHARLES HOLMES 1868-1936
314 Keswick Mountains 1921
    Oil on canvas 46 x 81.7 cm.
    Manchester City Art Gallery

JAMES DURDEN 1878-1964
315 Summer in Cumberland (the artist's
    house under Skiddaw) 1925
    Oil on canvas 101.5 x 101.5 cm.
    Manchester City Art Gallery

NELSON WRIGHT d. 1930
316 A Cumberland Slate Quarry 1926
    Oil on canvas 63.6 x 76.4 cm.
    Manchester City Art Gallery

BEN NICHOLSON b. 1894
317 Cumbrian Landscape
    (version 2) 1928
    Oil on canvas
    Wilfred Roberts Esq.

WINIFRED NICHOLSON b. 1893
318 Boothby Bank
    Oil on canvas
    61.6 x 61cm.
    Manchester City Art Gallery

F. BATESON MASON b. 1910
319 Great Gable and Wastwater 1937
    Oil on canvas
    66.3 x 91.5 cm.
    Manchester City Art Gallery

DELMAR BANNER
320 View from Scafell 1945
    Oil on canvas
    Mrs. Josephine Banner

GILBERT SPENCER 1893-1979
321 Little Langdale 1946
    Watercolour 56 x 77 cm.
    Birmingham Museum and
    Art Gallery

KURT SCHWITTERS 1887-1948
322 Merzbau Wall 1947-8
  ○ Photograph by courtesy of the
    Hatton Gallery
    University of Newcastle Upon Tyne
Schwitters, a refugee from the outside
world in a sense undreamed of by the
Arcadian settlers, began taking holidays
in the Lake District in 1943. He settled in
Ambleside in 1945. At the house of an
acquaintance Mr Harry Pierce of
Walthwaite House, Langdale,
Schwitters began his third *Merzbau* – the
first in Hanover having been destroyed
in an Allied air raid in 1943, and the
second, constructed when Schwitters
was a refugee in Norway, still intact in
1944 but shortly to be destroyed in an
accidental fire of 1951.

The Langdale structure, removed in
1965 to the Hatton Gallery in the
University of Newcastle, is thus the sole
remaining sculpture by Schwitters in
this post-Dada idiom that employs the
pasted up detritus of civilization.

Aesthetically, it is a document of Lake
District culture history analagous to
Wordsworth's Preface to the *Lyrical
Ballads*.

321

DAVID NASH b.1945
323 Wooden Waterway Grizedale Forest
    Photograph (Gelatin-Silver print)
    and drawing
    Property of the artist

JON GROOM b.1945
324 Living Blue
    Oil and beeswax on wood
    29.2 x 33 cm.
    Property of the artist
Jon Groom's fastidious work has
beginnings in closely observed qualities
he selects from a specific landscape. His
experience of the natural properties of a
place, however – the colour and density
of rock, the immateriality of water or
atmosphere – is mediated in the later
performance of the painting by his
emotional recollections of that place,
and by the formal contingencies that
arrive in the painting process.

325

ANDY GOLDSWORTHY b.1956
325 Icicle, broken in two, frozen to rock
    with spit
    Brough 14 January 1982
    Photograph (Cibachrome)
    40.7 x 30.5 cm.
    Property of the artist

326 Bracken Fronds Brough 1982
    Photograph (Cibachrome)
    40.7 x 30.5 cm.
    Property of the artist
Andy Goldsworthy works only with
natural materials. His ephemeral
sculptures suggest an organic unity of
man in nature, for he thinks of the
products of his own body – in this case
saliva – as natural. In some ways we may
then see his re-arrangement and
re-ordering of these materials as a
natural event, and the photograph as a
document of their growth and decay.

A SORT OF NATIONAL PROPERTY: PARTICIPATION AND CONSERVATION

PARTICIPATION Around 1800, the characteristic posture of the man communing with landscape changed from that of prospect hunter, who stood at one of the stations appointed by West or Crosthwaite. From Wordsworth, flat on his back beside a wall in the Hollens Wood above Dove Cottage, to Ruskin tracing the branches of a tree against the sky at Fontainebleau, romantics sought the relaxed self abandoning physical state of the Rousseauesque trance to achieve spiritual insight. Such moments were isolated in days of strenuous physical and intellectual activity, and were probably achieved only on the condition that the whole organism was in

327

some way racing. Coleridge's experience on Scafell, perhaps an extreme example of the romantic interest in extreme situations and extreme modes of feeling, tells us much not only about himself and his generation, but about the origins and subsequent culture of mountaineering and other risk laden sports.

Coleridge had met Sara Hutchinson almost three years before writing this letter to her. He had inconveniently fallen in love with her, arguably to the detriment of his own marriage. His narrative is masterly:

There is one sort of Gambling, to which I am much addicted; and that not of the least criminal kind for a man who has children and a Concern. – It is this. When I find it convenient to descend from a mountain, I am too confident and too indolent to look round about and wind about 'till I find a track or other symptom of safety; but I wander on, and where it is first possible to descend, there I go – relying upon fortune for how far down this possibility will continue. So it was yesterday afternoon. I passed down from Broadcrag, skirted the Precipices, and found myself cut off from a most sublime Crag-sumit, that seemed to rival Sca'Fell Man in height, and to outdo it in fierceness. A Ridge of Hill lay low down, and divided this Crag (called Doe-crag) and Broad-crag – even as the Hyphen divided the words broad and crag. I determined to go thither; the first place I came to, that was not direct Rock, I slipped down, and went on for a while with tolerable ease – but now I came (it was midway down) to a smooth perpendicular Rock about 7 feet high – this was nothing – I put my hands on the Ledge, and dropped down / in a few yards came just such another / I dropped that too / and yet another, seemed not higher – I would not stand for a trifle / so I dropped that too / but the stretching of the muscle(s) of my hands and arms, and the jolt of the Fall on my Feet, put my whole Limbs in a Tremble, and I paused, and looking down, saw that I had little else to encounter but a succession of these little Precipices – it was in truth a Path that in very hard Rain is, no doubt, the channel of a most splendid Waterfall. – So I began to suspect that I ought not to go on / but then unfortunately tho' I could with ease drop down a smooth Rock 7 feet high, I could not climb it / so go on I must / and on I went / the next 3 drops were not half a Foot, at least not a foot more than my own height / but every Drop increased the Palsy of my Limbs – I shook all over, Heaven knows without the least influence of Fear / and now I had only two more to drop down / to return was impossible – but of these two the first was tremendous / it was twice my own height, and the Ledge at the bottom was (so) exceedingly narrow, that if I dropt down upon it I must of necessity have fallen backwards and of course killed myself.
My Limbs were all in a tremble – I lay upon my Back to rest myself, and was beginning according to my Custom to laugh at myself for a Madman, when the sight of the Crags above me on each side, and the impetuous Clouds just over them, posting so luridly and so rapidly northward, overawed me / I lay in a state of almost prophetic Trance and Delight – and blessed God aloud, for the powers of

344

Reason and the Will, which remaining no Danger can overpower us!
O God, I exclaimed aloud – how calm, how blessed am I now / I
know not how to proceed, how to return / but I am calm and fearless
and confident / if this Reality were a Dream, if I were asleep, what
agonies had I suffered! what screams! when the Reason and the Will
are away, what remains to us but Darkness and Dimness and a
bewildering Shame, and Pain that is utterly Lord over us, or fantastic
Pleasure, that draws the Soul along swimming through the air in
many shapes, even as a Flight of Starlings in a Wind.
I arose and looking down saw at the bottom a heap of Stones – which
had fallen abroad – and rendered the narrow Ledge on which they
had been piled, doubly dangerous / at the bottom of the third Rock
that I dropt from, I met a dead Sheep quite rotten – This heap of
Stones, I guessed, and have since found that I guessed aright, had
been piled up by the Shepherd to enable him to climb up and free the
poor creature whom he had observed to be crag-fast – but seeing
nothing but rock over rock, he had desisted and gone for help – and
in the mean time the poor creature had fallen down and killed itself. –
As I was looking at these I glanced my eye to my left, and observed
that the Rock was rent from top to bottom – I measured the breadth
of the Rent, and found that there was no danger of my being wedged
in / so I put my Knap-sack round to my side, and slipped down as
between two walls, without any danger or difficulty – the next Drop
brought me down on the Ridge called the How / I hunted out my
Besom Stick, which I had flung before me when I first came to the
Rocks – and wisely gave over all thoughts of ascending Doe-Crag –
for now the Clouds were again coming in most tumultously – so I
began to descend / when I felt an odd sensation across my whole
Breast – not pain nor itching – and putting my hand on it I found it
all bumpy – and on looking saw the whole of my Breast from my
Neck (to my Navel) – and exactly all that my Kamell-hair
Breast-shield covers, filled with great red heat-bumps, so thick that
no hair could lie between them.
6 August 1802
Coleridge Letters, ed. E.L. Griggs, 1956, 11

327 Coleridge by George Dance 1804
   Photograph of drawing
   Trustees of Dove Cottage

328 Descent of Broad Stand c.1900
   Photograph Abraham Brothers
   Sidney Cross Esq.

329 Scafell from Napes Ridge
   Photograph Abraham Brothers
   Alpine Club

Coleridge's descent here was of Broad Stand, a route that still figures in
the modern rock climber's catalogue. The element of risk, and the casual
unpremeditated nature of the enterprise were clearly fundamental to the
adventure, and it is this same aspect that emerges when, some eighty
years later, the modern sport was brought back to the Lake District by
Haskett Smith, Owen Glynne Jones and other members of the Alpine
Club.

   Climbing, the sport of young men from the universities, was
publicised by Jones's accounts; his classic *Rock Climbing in the English
Lake District* came out in 1897, illustrated with photographs taken by two
local men, the brothers Ashley and George Abraham. After Jones's death
in 1899, the Abrahams themselves produced detailed accounts of climbs,
their inspirational photographs dramatising the sport and emphasising its
high spirituality while offering as exact an account as possible of routes
and techniques. The element of rhetoric in these photographs, and of a
tendency to melodrama in their writing, perhaps embarrassed the laconic
élite of the Alpine Club. Yet for that reason nonetheless the Abraham
images remain brilliant and curiously intimate documents of the
romantic cult of mountains in its nineteenth century development.

330 A Party of Three ascending the Needle gully, Gt. Gable
   Photograph Abraham Brothers: modern contact print
   Fell and Rock Climbing Club and Abbot Hall
This party of scramblers carry the traditional ice-axe. Ladies wore
long skirts when climbing until the First World War.

Climbing snow filled gulleys in the Lake District provided winter
practice for those preparing for summer ascents in the Alps. This
developed into summer scrambling up those same gulleys. Not until
Haskett Smith, a year after being introduced to the Lake District on an
undergraduate reading party from Oxford, decided in the summer of
1882 to climb Pillar, did climbing for its own sake begin.

There are recorded climbs by shepherds up Pillar before 1882, by the Old
West route, but Haskett Smith climbed Pillar by two new routes (and
attempted a third). His concern was with the climb and not with simply
reaching the top.

331 The West Face of Pillar Rock

  Photograph Abraham Brothers
  Fell and Rock Climbing Club and Abbot Hall
Pillar Rock stands above Ennerdale on the north side of Pillar
Mountain – it is impossible to reach the summit without using one's
hands.

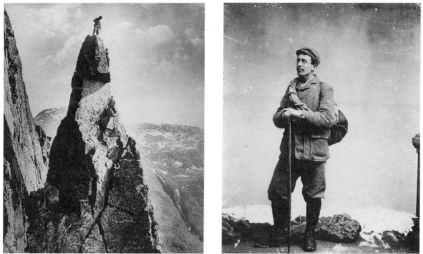

332

333

332 Napes Needle
  Photograph Abraham Brothers; reproduction of original print
  Fell and Rock Climbing Club and Abbot Hall
In 1884 Haskett Smith made a famous ascent of Napes Needle on Great
Gable. Rock climbing had arrived as a major sport in the Lake District.
People began to climb up rock faces in summer rather than scrambling
up gulleys in winter as practice for the Alps.

333 Owen Glynne Jones – ready for climbing
  Photograph Abraham Brothers; reproduction from original print
  Fell and Rock Climbing Club and Abbot Hall
Owen Glynne Jones (after proving himself an innovative climber in his
native Wales) first came to the Lake District during Easter 1890, armed
only with guides prepared for fell walkers (he possessed Herman Prior's
guide of 1865, and it is clear that others he met were using guides by
Baddely and by Jenkinson).
  Jones and his friend Dr. Sumpner walking from Langdale to the top of
Scafell Pike, and then on an impulse attempted to climb Scafell itself by
way of Broad Stand. In his account Jones reprimands himself for his
foolhardiness in attempting such a climb without a rope: to emphasize
that point he observes that the ground was covered by snow and ice.

334 Broad Stand from Mickledore
  Photograph Abraham Brothers; modern contact print
  Fell and Rock Climbing Club and Abbot Hall

By 1896, Jones's genius for climbing in the Lake District was established; his meeting in that year with the Abraham brothers, two young photographers from Keswick, led to the popularisation of rock climbing. The brothers realised that here was an exciting new subject for photography; and Jones found a new method of illustrating the route of each climb and something of its unique, even dramatic excitement.

"We composed our limbs to a photographic quiescence" Jones commented. His account brings home the energy and artfulness that such a photograph then demanded:

'Ashley had a splendid wide-angle lens, which, from his elevated position on the traverse opposite, could take in 400 feet of the summit. It was his turn to take the lead. 'Mr. Jones! I can't see you, your clothes are so dark'. I apologised. 'Will you step out a foot or two from that hole?' I was in a cheerful mood and ready to oblige a friend, but the platform was scarcely two feet square, and to acquiesce was to step out a few hundred feet into Deep Ghyll. For this I had not made adequate preparation and told him so. 'Well, will you take off your coat?' That I could do with pleasure, and for a while his instructions were levelled at George.

He was in an awkward place and was much cramped in ensuring safety, but Ashley was dissatisfied and insisted on his lifting the left leg. This gave him no foothold to speak of, but in the cause of photography he had been trained to manage without such ordinary aids. He grumbled a little at the inconvenience but obeyed, resolving that it he were living when the next slide was to be exposed he himself would be the manipulator and his brother the centre of the picture. The ghyll had become rather gloomy and we had a lengthy exposure. I was glad to slip on my jacket again and draw in the rope for George's ascent.'

335 Scafell Pinnacle from Deep Ghyll, the curving crack
    Owen Glynne Jones and George Abraham
    Photograph Ashley Abraham; modern contact print
    Fell and Rock Climbing Club and Abbot Hall
The Fell and Rock Climbing Club of the English Lake District was founded in 1906 to encourage the pursuit of fell walking and of rock climbing, and at the same time to protect "the amenities of the district". Ashley Abraham was the first president. It was the Fell and Rock Climbing Club which negotiated the purchase of 3,000 acres of Wasdale including the peak of Great Gable and presented them to the National Trust in 1923 as a memorial to their members killed in the First World War. (Common rights effectively reduced the gift to 1,183 acres).

336 Wasdale
    Photograph Abraham Brothers; modern contact print from original negative
    Fell and Rock Climbing Club and Abbot Hall
    Note the plate has not been completely retouched: the woman in the boat is in the process of being removed to increase the sense that the beholder alone possesses a vast solitude.

336

Most of the high land on this photograph (excepting Yewbarrow on the left) makes up the gift; from left to right, the mountains are: Yewbarrow, Kirkfell, Great Gable (in centre), Lingmell. Scafell can be reached by climbing the righthand slopes.

Much of the drama of mountains is inherent in them, as is the heroic element of rock climbing, and the photographer would find it both difficult and perverse to avoid reporting on it. The preference among rock climbers for a less dramatic reportage, more in keeping with their personal style and with the verbal accounts in their manuals, led to the adoption of drawing to illustrate the later manuals. The best examples of austere draughtsmanship, virtually diagrammatic in their clipped address to the problem in hand, are the drawings of W. Heaton Cooper, himself an experienced climber, made for the Fell and Rock Climbing Club in the 1930's. Cooper's revision of the original photographically illustrated series is still standard.

337 The West Face of Pillar, marked to show a route
    Photograph Abraham Brothers
    Alpine Club
For the climber, the dramatic aspect in peripheral, and arguably the photograph, especially taken with the wide angle lens, includes too much of the splendid surroundings: good for the spectator, less so for the route finder.

338 W. HEATON COOPER (living)
    The West Face of Pillar Rock
    Pencil 25.5 x 20.4 cm.
    Sidney Cross Esq.

Climbing was only a part of the growing demand for access to wild and unspoilt areas, a demand that came from all sections of society. Between the two world wars, new organisations were set up: the Council for the Preservation of Rural England in 1926, the Youth Hostel Association in 1929, the Friends of the Lake District in 1934 and the Ramblers Association in 1935. Immediately after the war the wish to proselytise strenuous and sanitive involvement with landscape among the young led to the setting up of outdoor centres such as Outward Bound; and today the right of everyone to an active experience of the Lake District is symbolised by the foundation in 1976 of the Calvert Trust, an outdoor centre for the disabled on the shores of Bassenthwaite. The strength of public opinion and pressure from such organisations has persuaded successive governments since the war to set up and develop the machinery of National Parks. The Lake District was, with the Peak District, in 1951 the first of the National Parks.

339 Wray Castle 1931
    Photograph
    Youth Hostel Association
Wray Castle, on the western shore of Windermere, was in 1931 one of the first Youth Hostels to be established in the Lake District. By 1933, the castle was leased by its owner, The National Trust, to the Freshwater Biological Association.

It was in 1946 that Outward Bound was founded – Kurt Hahn, a refugee from Nazism and the founder of distinguished schools at Salem in Germany and Gordonstoun in Scotland, was the initiator of the scheme at Aberdovey, Wales in 1941. The Lake District provided two sites, one in Eskdale and the other on Ullswater (Halsteads, a house built by Wordsworth's friend John Marshall in the early nineteenth century). Outward Bound's aim was to promote personal development in young people; the high moral tone of these founding years was emphasised in the early publicity photographs. A belief in the healing and teaching qualities of nature is implicit.

340 "Morning Prayers are held wherever the boys may be"
Photograph
The Outward Bound Trust

341 "Outward Bound character training:
The patrol pauses during a strenuous sixty mile expedition to wonder at the vastness and the beauty"
Photograph
The Outward Bound Trust

341

342

342 A girl rock climber
Photograph
The Outward Bound Trust
This photograph of about 1960 publicised the first Outward Bound courses for girls, and emphasized that girls should participate fully in both the ethic of self discovery and in the activities of the movement. Clothing, equipment and technique have all changed during the past 25 years.

Outward Bound and Brathay Hall Trust immediately after the war were among the first to set up outdoor activity centres in the Lake District. Today, forty years on, there are over a hundred such centres. They illustrate the assimilation of the large family houses which were built in the late eighteenth and early nineteenth centuries to present needs for mass accommodation. Educational authorities and trusts own such buildings and they are testament to the continuing Wordsworthian doctrine that nature can teach. The institutions vary their emphasis from physical activity to field studies sometimes at a high intellectual level.

343 The Outward Bound Training Centre at Eskdale
o Photograph c. 1975
   The Outward Bound Trust
The house, called The Gatehouse, was built for J. H. Rea, later Baron, in 1896-1904 by A. Huddart of Whitehaven. It was sold up in 1949, and opened by Outward Bound in 1950. For the simple and dramatic contrast between the nineteenth century use of such houses, and that brought about by their institutionalization, compare this image with no. 285 or 293.

344 Calvert Trust expedition to the top of Latrigg, Skiddaw in
o the background
   Photograph July 1975
   The Calvert Trust
A recent and wholly welcome development has been the Calvert Trust Challenge for the Disabled, which provides residential opportunities for the disabled to take part in canoeing, sailing, bird watching, riding, even wheel chairing down mountains. One of their Lake District sites is Little Crosthwaite, a farm on the banks of Bassenthwaite; and the other is Old Windy Brow, a farm house with barn and stables near Keswick where Wordsworth and his sister lived in 1795, the guests of William and Raisley Calvert.

CONSERVATION

After the coming of the railway to Windermere in 1847, the assaults on the Lake District for a time seemed less "rash". Access to the fells and to footpaths threatened with closure became a widespread even popular concern. In the 1870's, Manchester Corporation decided it must have a better water supply for the rapidly growing city. It looked to the Lakes, and, having first bought the Thirlmere catchment area, applied to Parliament in 1877 for powers to construct a reservoir and take fifty million gallons a day by aqueduct to Manchester. It was a bold scheme. Immediately, fierce opposition was aroused. Thirlmere was arguably *the* central lake – a lovely natural place – the inspiration of major poets and painters. The photographs show Thirlmere as it was in 1879, the year in which Parliament granted its approval to the scheme. The two pools of water, joined at the idiosyncratic bridge, were surrounded by fine deciduous woods, a few sheep farms and the dominating height of Helvellyn – an image infinitely suggestive, but for Wordsworth the very epitome of his humanism.

345 Thirlmere looking north 1879
   Photograph: modern reproduction from original print
   North West Water Authority

346 Thirlmere looking south 1879
   Photograph; modern reproduction from original print
   North West Water Authority

The Thirlmere Defence Association was formed in September 1877. An article in the Spectator supported this opposition: "What is more truly sanitary to a busy people than the solitude and lovliness of the few natural gardens in which they can forget the thick atmosphere and incessant noise of City life?" (8 September 1877). William Morris, Thomas Carlyle, John Ruskin (now at Coniston) opposed Manchester: two prominent campaigners were Octavia Hill and Canon Rawnsley, both later to be founders of the National Trust. It was the massiveness of the scheme against "one of England's chief recreation grounds" which appalled the Bishop of Carlisle; the minor water abstraction from

345

348

Ennerdale by Whitehaven in 1849 had not tampered "with the features of the valley", and so, to the Bishop, that had been acceptable.
   Opposition proved vain and the scheme was approved by Parliament in 1879. The damage to natural beauty was severe. A new road, the now familiar A591 from Grasmere, was cut through the rock high along the

mountain side; and when local people objected to the damage caused by construction traffic, another, now unnecessary road was built on the western shore in 1889. The natural water level had fluctuated by only a few feet; under the artificial regime, it rises and falls about thirty feet, leaving a moonscape of bare stones. A further blow came in 1908 when Manchester planted nearly two thousand acres of conifers. They could have planted broad leaved trees, but the contemporary belief was that this would pollute the water supply, so pure that until recently it passed straight into the taps at Manchester. This economy in not providing a purification plant meant that the public had to be kept away from the water, a situation now remedied by the building in 1982 of a water treatment works. For the first time in a hundred years a new opportunity for development of Thirlmere as a recreation site exists.

347 Thirlmere looking north from near Launch Gill
    Showing Raven Crag, and the cutting of the new road
    Photograph
    North West Water Authority

348 Thirlmere looking north 1984
    Photograph David Lyons

349 Thirlmere looking south 1984
    Photograph David Lyons

350 The Rock of Names c.1880
    Photograph anonymous
    Trustees of Dove Cottage

Thirlmere was well known to both Coleridge and Wordsworth. The "Rock of Names" was the meeting place between Coleridge's home at Keswick and Wordsworth's at Grasmere. On this rock, on Coleridge's initiative, the initials of six friends had been engraved: Wordsworth, his future wife Mary Hutchinson, his sister Dorothy, Coleridge, John Wordsworth and Sara Hutchinson. During construction of the reservoir the rock was blown up. The fragments rescued by Canon Rawnsley were cemented into a small pyramid of stone, immediately above the new roadside. In 1984, following two nearby landslides and the prospect of extensive tree felling of the now mature conifers, it was arranged that the fragments should be embedded in a single rockface (as they originally had been) and then set into the quarry face immediately behind Dove Cottage and the new museum.

For the first time, a public body had, on a large scale, destroyed natural beauty and denied public access to a large area of the fells. There was a moral dilemma for some. Canon Rawnsley, for instance, appears to have accepted the need for people in Manchester to have a supply of pure water, and his objection was muted. Others were more vociferous: – the "vandals" of Manchester were set against the "sentimentalists" of the Defence Society. At the opening of the reservoir 12 October 1894, Canon Rawnsley opened the proceedings with a lengthy prayer:

...Let this river of God flow through the far off city to cleanse and purify; to help and heal. Pour it with full refreshment for the bodies of our fellow townsmen. Speed it with light and joy and gladness for their souls. Send it with cheer and comfort to their homes, with health and life into their dwellings...

351 Memorial card issued to mark the opening ceremony 12 October
○ 1894 of the Thirlmere Reservoir
Lithograph printed in colour
North West Water Authority

Sir John Harwood, the chairman of the Water Board and chief artificer of the scheme, had no doubts about its utilitarian and aesthetic success:
You imagined that we were about to transform all that delighted you into the semblance of the mill dam, and you fought as stoutly, as Englishmen always fight. Well, we won, and Parliament empowered us to execute these works and appropriate this lake, minding us, however, to be careful how we proceeded... We invite and challenge inspection... Is there anything hideous in the handsome embankment we have formed? Is there one of you who thinks that jaded men and women, who seek restoration to health and strength in the quiet contemplation of the unspeakable beauties of Nature, will be deterred from seeking all they need in this sequestered region because we have applied this watershed to purposes of civilisation? No; a thousand times no.
The Manchester view was 'that the corporation had, in fact, "improved Nature"'. Most of the speakers in a variety of ways echoed the pledge given by Sir John Hibbert:
It was their duty, having drawn upon the district for their water supply, to recognise the obligation that rested upon them to preserve its natural beauties.

352 The Whitsuntide Walk of the Friendly Societies c.1880
Photograph anonymous
The Ruskin Museum Coniston
This walk, by which the self help movement of the great northern cities extended its members' cultural and spiritual horizons into the Lake District, was held annually in Coniston from the 1830's. Coincidentally but with some symbolic relevance to events in Thirlmere, the walk was discontinued in 1894.

It was this act of Manchester, more than any other, which was to provide the major impetus for the formation of such bodies as the Friends of the Lake District (the regional branch of the Council for the Preservation of Rural England), and the National Trust. Fights against the bringing of railways to the Honister slate quarry and to the Ennerdale iron ore mine, the rash proposal to extend the Windermere railway to Ambleside and attempts to close footpaths up Latrigg at Keswick led Rawnsley in the 1883 meeting of the Wordsworth Society, with Matthew Arnold in the chair, to propose the Lake District Defence Society.

In 1894, in a separate move, Rawnsley and others also set up the National Trust to hold land and thus protect it from unsuitable development. From the start, the National Trust was constituted as a relatively passive organisation concerned with the acquisition and management of the land, while the more vocal opposition came from the Defence Society. Even so their roles were not yet sharply divided; in 1919, the Defence Society was reformed to become the Lake District Safeguarding Society, confined to landowners. But more was needed, and in 1934, under the stimulus of massive forestry developments, the society was reconstituted with wider interests as the Friends of the Lake District.

Although the Friends was an active body fighting for conservation and protecting access, it too bought land and, in 1937, it set up a company, Lake District Farm Estates, to acquire and maintain traditional farming and farm buildings. Its chairman was then Francis Scott, of the Provincial Insurance Company. In the 1940's it owned almost two thousand acres, but by 1977 this had all been transferred to the National Trust. Thus, the two bodies again complement each other, the National Trust protecting land by ownership and covenant, and the Friends of the Lake District by active campaigning whenever a need arises.

353 A Group of Publicity Booklets relating to the founding of
    The Defence Society
    The Friends of the Lake District
    The National Trust

354 Map showing land held by the National Trust in 1944 and in 1984
    The Lake District Special Planning Board
The National Trust was set up in 1895 to hold permanently land and buildings for the benefit of the nation. In 1907 it was reformed as a body corporate by act of parliament, and its affairs are now controlled by a succession of acts. From 1907, the Trust could declare land inalienable, thus safeguarding it forever. This legal claim to perpetuity is one of the special characteristics of the Trust; it persuades owners that the Trust can ensure a permanent public benefit, but it imposes on the Trust a massive and extremely burdensome responsibility. In recent years, the Trust's holdings in the Lake District have greatly increased. By 1944, the Trust owned over seventeen thousand acres in the Lake District (four thousand of which had been given by Mrs. Heelis – Beatrix Potter), but, after the war, the holding expanded rapidly to 122,000 acres, one quarter of the national park.

355 The Seventeenth Century Coniston Old Hall
    Before 1973
    Photograph
    The National Trust

356 The Seventeenth Century Coniston Old Hall
    During restoration late 1975
    Photograph The National Trust

357 The Seventeenth Century Coniston Old Hall
    Today 1984
    Photograph
    The National Trust

The National Trust has a concern for places of historic interest or natural beauty. Although the major burden is the preservation of landscape, the Trust has to maintain important architectural buildings such as the seventeenth century Coniston Old Hall or a mid-nineteenth century gothic masterpiece such as Wray Castle. The restoration of Coniston Old Hall began in 1973 and has continued, in stages, for ten years. As the buildings had not been much modernised, the restorers found that many of the early features were undisturbed.

358

358 Townend Troutbeck
    Photograph c. 1900
    The National Trust

359 Townend Troutbeck
    Photograph c. 1950
    The National Trust

360 Townend Troutbeck
 ○ Photograph 1984
    The National Trust

The house of the Browne family is one of the finest examples of a large statesman house in the Lake District. It was built c. 1626 and contains carved woodwork as well as the books, papers and furniture used by the Browne family who lived there until 1944. The photographs show what to some may seem a minor aesthetic detail, but one that represents the whole range of problems inherent in the sympathetic management of such properties, with a long history of occupation and alteration. How should the garden and its gate be restored? The photographs show the nineteenth century gate made of interwoven yew boughs; then the gate that replaced it; and finally the new gate, constructed in 1984 and paid for by the Friends of the Lake District. The colour of the house remains a problem.

361 Rydal House 1984
  ○ Photograph Robert Thrift
    The National Trust

362 Rydal House with close up of wall 1984
    Photograph Robert Thrift
    The National Trust

In order to prepare for restoration work, the National Trust records the older colourings that are gradually disappearing. The photographs show a house in Rydal with a close up of the coloured surface. In 1945, Rydal was still almost wholly in the possession of the le Fleming family and was a quiet yellow ochre lime washed hamlet. Under increasing individual ownership, the former colouring has been replaced by white, or occasionally even grey. The use of modern paints can have unexpected and disastrous results; it seals the surface, thus prevents the house from "breathing", and, in time, the render, or harling, becomes waterlogged; both paint and harling then fall off. The National Trust is discovering that the best finish for rendered farmhouses in lime wash, for it allows the houses to breathe and dry out. An aesthetic consideration is that lime wash, whether white or coloured, pleasingly varies its tint with changes in the weather. Even in Rydal today, it would be possible to restore the ochre lime wash, now one of its lost glories.

363 The Gondola
  ○ Photograph Robert Thrift
    The National Trust

The Gondola was renovated by the National Trust in 1980 and ran its first complete season on the lake in 1981. It is a steam yacht, originally launched in 1859 and then left to rot in the grounds of Coniston Waterhead until given to the Trust by Mr. Arthur Hatton. It restores to Coniston Water something of the Italianate festival aura of the Arcadian epoch, mediated through the steam age. Coniston Old Man towers above, and on the shore line is seen some of the traditional broad leafed forest, one of nature's triumphs in the central Lake District. The Trust has been active in preserving and replanting broad leafed trees and has now taken on exceptional responsibilities for the great woodlands in the Borrowdale valley.

364 Claife Station July 1983
    Photograph Robert Thrift
    The National Trust

This natural platform above Ferry Point on the west side of Windermere was named by Thomas West in 1778 as his first Station on Lake Windermere, the vital first formal introduction to the Lake District experience. The trees have grown so tall that the views are no longer visible and the building is a ruin, but the Countryside Commission has offered a grant to the National Trust to enable it to plan for the future use of the site in a way that is historically sensitive and practical. In order to do the necessary research the Trust is seeking photographs of the building before it became a ruin. The photograph shown at no. 50 for

364

example was only recently recognised as an important record of the building before its collapse.

365 Stool End Farm May 1984
    Photograph Robert Thrift
    The National Trust
New farming methods require new buildings. The Trust decided that it would build a new barn, but with traditional materials.

366 Langdale Pikes from Harry Place April 1984
    Photograph Robert Thrift
    The National Trust

367 Leaflet advertising the Lake District
    Landscape Fund, launched 1984
    The National Trust

The major part of the National Trust's work in the Lake District is the preservation of traditional landscapes. The maintenance of stone walls, and of the whole distinctive pattern on the landscape of the pastoral economy, is a policy which sometimes has to defy simple commercial forces. The magnitude of the problem of trying to maintain a landscape as outlined in the National Trust's leaflet establishes the need for the special Lake District Landscape Fund. The National Trust is acutely aware that to maintain its responsibilities requires money not only for materials but also for the manpower to serve, protect and guide the public. In addition to wardens, craftsmen and others skilled in traditional rural industries are necessary to maintain and restore the quality of landscape and life of those parts of the Lake District that the Trust holds for the public benefit.

THE NORTHERN
ARCADIA AND ITS USES

Consciousness of the Lake District as Arcadia and of the whole classical landscape tradition by which the district originally made its claim to greatness is now not widespread, but the process which connects the present to the past only emphasises the continuity of concern for the landscape, for its material and spiritual riches, which can be increased by skilfull use or easily destroyed. Informal authority in these matters, once exercised by landowners and writers, was strengthened and given popular weight by the voluntary movements of concerned people founded in the late nineteenth century. In the present, authority over the appearance and use of the landscape has characteristically been assumed by Parliament, and the complicated, often conflicting interests of citizens in a democracy are presided over by a network of statutory institutions.

THE PROBLEM

After the construction of Thirlmere, Manchester Corporation left the Lake District alone until it promoted a private Bill in 1919 to buy the catchments of Mardale, Swindale and Wet Sleddale (24,000 acres). New reservoirs were authorised in all 3 dales. Haweswater was completed in 1939 after many delays and Wet Sleddale was built in 1966. The powers to build in Swindale were transferred to the North West Water Authority when that body was set up in 1974 and are still available. The water from all this catchment goes by aqueduct down Long Sleddale to join the Thirlmere pipeline.

368

368 Haweswater from Harter Fell showing draw down
   Photograph Geoffrey Berry

369 A591 looking North towards St. John's Vale: Saddleback in
   the distance
   Traffic speeding through the centre of the Lake District
   Photograph Geoffrey Berry

Widening of the A591 from Windermere through Rydal and
Grasmere to Keswick has been strongly contested, with only limited
success, since the Ministry of Transport first proposed it in 1931. It was
often used as an alternative to the A6 over Shap. The Friends of the Lake
District argued strongly that the right answer was to improve the trunk
roads on the west coast and over Shap. The A591 was the responsibility
of two highway authorities, Westmorland and Cumberland County
Councils.

   Westmorland was more sensitive to natural beauty than Cumberland
so that the stretch from Windermere to Grasmere is only slightly
improved, compared with the stretch in Cumberland from Thirlmere to
Keswick, which is now dual carriageway and harshly urban in
appearance. Regrettably, resolution weakened under the post war traffic
boom and despite establishment of the National Park Westmorland
drove a dual carriageway over Dunmail Raise in 1971.

370 Summit of Hardknott Pass
   looking East towards Wrynose
   A traffic jam in a lonely place c. 1972
   Photograph Geoffrey Berry

In the Lake District, valleys radiate from a central core of high mountains
cut by high level passes. It is not well understood that until 1934, there
were no roads suitable for motors over the high passes except at Dunmail
Raise and at Kirkstone. In 1934, the Cumberland County Council
proposed to the Government Commissioners for this special area of West
Cumberland that new roads should be built over:
1. Honister
2. Sty Head between Gable and Scafell
3. Wrynose and Hardknott
4. Dunnerdale to Waberthwaite
5. Dunnerdale to Eskdale
Their liberal-Keynsian intent was to create jobs for the unemployed and
open up the country to tourism.

   Despite a petition by 11,000 people, and the refusal of grants from the
Government Commissioners, the County Council went ahead and built
the Honister Road (with a grant from the Minister of Transport) and
carried out limited improvements to the Dunnerdale Eskdale Road. The
others were dropped, except that on a minimum cost basis, the County
Council laid tarmac over the old tracks on the Hardknott-Wrynose pass,
and this is the road which inappropriately attracts motorists today. In
1937, in the next round, the County Council succeeded in forcing a new
road over Newlands from Braithwaite to Buttermere.

371 A formal army of conifers skirts Pillar
   Photograph Geoffrey Berry

Some of the earliest and most famous rock climbs are on Pillar (2927ft), a
fine mountain diminished in beauty and stature by conifers and timber
extraction roads and now difficult to reach. Planting of this land by the
Forestry Commission in the early 1930's was almost universally
deplored. Wordsworth did not like larch – "ten thousand of this spiky
tree, the larch, are stuck at once upon the side of a hill: they can grow up
into nothing but deformity" he wrote. A few landowers were making
small plantations early in the nineteenth century but they barely changed
the landscape until the Forestry Commission came along in 1919,
charged by Government to built up a reserve of timber and to provide
jobs in rural areas, especially those within 15 miles of the 'Special Areas'
of high unemployment, such as west Cumbria. By the end of 1933 the
Commission had planted in the Lake District almost 1¼ million larch
and over 5 million spruce.

371

372 Upper Eskdale, Bowfell in centre background
   The sweeping slopes on the right were to have been afforested
   Photograph Geoffrey Berry

In 1935 the Forestry Commission bought 7000 acres in Eskdale and
Dunnerdale and proposed to create the Hardknott Forest Park. The
proposals inspired a national controversy and debates in Parliament. The
newly formed Friends of the Lake District offered to buy the land back at
cost; protracted negotiations resulted in an agreement in 1938 that the
Friends would compensate the Forestry Commission at the rate of £2 per
acre for not planting 240 acres in Eskdale. The 5000 acres of unplantable
land were to be covenanted to the National Trust to preserve them from
development and safeguard access. In 1942 the Forestry Commission
went back on this undertaking to covenant, but renewed pressure
eventually led them to drop the Forest Park idea in 1945. Unfortunately
the Council for the Preservation of Rural England and Friends of the
Lake District were unable to save the upper parts of Dunnerdale on
Harter Fell.

373 This map of 1936 specifies the central area of the Lake District
   protected from afforestation; in the area shaded vertically it was not
   possible "to reach a clear cut demarcation between the claims of
   preservation and afforestation"

The national concern roused by the planting of Ennerdale in the 1930's,
the purchase of the Hardknott estate in 1934 and the active search by the
Forestry Commission for more land led to the setting up in April 1935 of
a joint committee of the Council for the Preservation of Rural England,
the Friends of the Lake District and the Forestry Commission. They
produced in 1936 an agreement, in an official White Paper, indicating in
the Lake District "a central block which, by reason of its unusual beauty
and seclusion and its remoteness, should be ruled out altogether from
afforestation by the Commissioners". That agreement, which still
stands, has protected the central Lake District from afforestation and is
today of fundamental importance to the Lake District Special Planning
Board in protecting the central area. It is clear from this diagram that
problems remain acute across the whole southern sweep, from Eskdale
in the west to Esthwaite and the head of Windermere in the east.

374 Greenside lead mine, closed in 1962
    Glenridding Ullswater
    Photograph Geoffrey Berry
Quarrying and mining are ancient industries and do not necessarily
destroy natural beauty. But rapid extraction with modern techniques
can, if unregulated, cause unintended erosion and create pollution. The
Greenside lead mine above Ullswater was acceptable when small but
large scale production in the 1930's led to the discharge of waste material
passing down the Red Tarn Beck into Ullswater of between 2 and 7 tons
per week, and the formation of a delta in the lake. The war, with an
urgent demand for lead, saved the mine owners from legal action. The
matter was resolved only when the vein was worked out in 1962.

375 1947 Hobhouse proposed a programme of National Parks   THE RESPONSIBLE
    – now largely completed   BODIES
    The proposed conservation areas are now designated as "Areas of
    Outstanding Natural Beauty"
National concern at the unregulated exploitation of land of the highest
natural beauty mounted steadily throughout the 30's and led to a series of
official reports:– the Scott Committee on Land Utilisation in Rural Areas
(Cmnd 6378), the Dower Report in 1945 on National Parks in England
and Wales (Cmnd 6628) and in 1947 the report of the National Parks
Committee (Cmnd 7121) chaired by Sir Arthur Hobhouse. John Dower
considered the theory and purpose of national park policy with reference
to Great Britain. He defined a national park as:–
    "an extensive area of beautiful and relatively wild country in which
    for the nation's benefit and by appropriate national decision and
    action, (a) the characteristic landscape beauty is strictly preserved, (b)
    access and facilities for public open air enjoyment are amply
    provided, (c) wildlife and buildings and places of architectural and
    historic interest are suitably protected, while (d) established farming
    use is effectively maintained".
This definition was accepted by the Hobhouse Committee which defined
potential national park boundaries.

376 Extract from Section 5, National Parks and Access to the
    Countryside Act 1949
The Government accepted the need for National Parks and in the
National Parks and Access to the Countryside Act 1949 set up a National
Parks Commission (now renamed the Countryside Commission)
charged *inter alia* to establish national parks in England and Wales. The
main purposes of National Parks were defined as preserving and
enhancing natural beauty and promoting their enjoyment by the public.
For the first time powers for planning control and the provision of access
were brought together in a local body charged by law to protect the
landscape. At national level the National Parks Commission was charged
not only to advise and support the national parks but to act as a national
watchdog to intervene in contentious issues, and as an advisor to the
Government on environmental matters.

377 Map showing the boundaries of the Lake District National Park, and
    its overlap of the local authority areas which have residual planning
    functions together with the Lake District Special Planning Board.
The National Parks Commission formally designated the Lake District
as a National Park in 1951. It was to be run by the Lake District Planning
Board, a joint committee of members of the three county councils of
Cumberland, Lancashire and Westmorland. Planning, highway and
other powers rested with those authorities with the consequential risk of
inconsistency between one part of the park and another. Upon local
government reorganisation in 1974 the Board was replaced by the more
independent Lake District Special Planning Board. It now has its own
planning powers though highways are still the responsibility of the new
Cumbria County Council and housing is administered by the 4 district
councils which overlap the Park. The cost of running the Park is met in
three ways: 10% comes from the ratepayers of Cumbria, 30% from
charges such as for car parks, and the remaining 60% comes from central
government in two ways – firstly 50% from a special national park
supplementary grant after advice from the Commission; secondly 10%
through the County Council by way of a rate support grant. Of the 30
members on the Board 16 are nominated by the County Council, 4 by
the Districts and 10 by the Secretary of State for the Environment after
advice from the Countryside Commission. How have these new bodies
coped with the problems which have faced them?

WATER   378 Map showing water abstraction schemes in the National Park
            The Lake District Special Planning Board
            Every major lake, with the exception of Coniston, now supplies
            water to meet our needs.
Resistance to water abstraction proposals has been reasonably successful,
but the pressure has not diminished. In 1961 the House of Lords rejected
Manchester Corporation's private Bill to secure powers over Ullswater.
The Minister of Housing and Local Government organised a thorough
review of the problem and Manchester put forward reduced proposals in
1965 to pump water from Ullswater and Windermere and pipe the
former by a new tunnel down Longsleddale. After a public inquiry the
Minister reluctantly allowed most of the proposals (but not the tunnel)
and said that Manchester should not "come back for more" on a plea of
urgent need.
    It looked as though there would be no more attacks on the Lakes,
especially when the North West Water Authority was set up in 1974 to
co-ordinate supplies over the whole of the North West. It was not to be.

379 Wastwater, showing natural shore line 1980
        Photograph David Lyons
A new threat emerged in 1978 when the North West Water Authority
supported by Cumbria County Council proposed to raise Ennerdale to
supply British Nuclear Fuels Limited at Windscale with very pure water.
Subsequently British Nuclear Fuels Limited submitted its own proposal
to raise the level of Wastwater. This was strongly resisted by the

Planning Board and Countryside Commission and considered at a public inquiry in 1980. The objectors were able to show that neither scheme was necessary and that a satisfactory supply could be obtained from the lower Derwent at an extra cost of some £10m. The developers were also urged to investigate a borehole supply. This time the Secretary of State for the Environment unequivocally rejected both schemes. Subsequently British Nuclear Fuels Limited found they could meet their needs from boreholes. The case amply justified the strong objections and demonstrated that a public enquiry is often the only way to investigate such proposals adequately.

However the future is not absolutely secure. In 1978 the North West Water Authority produced consultation proposals for 4 new reservoirs, one of which might be needed in the next century to supply the North West. They are an enlarged Haweswater and new reservoirs in Morecambe Bay, Borrowdale, and at Hellifield in Yorkshire.

380 The A593 from Coniston to Broughton   ROADS
    The road has been adapted to traffic needs without change of
    character by introducing passing places
    Photograph Geoffrey Berry c. 1970

Protection from damaging roads has been only moderately successful since 1951 because highway powers rest with the County Councils not the Special Planning Board. The Friends of the Lake District had first pressed for a roads policy in 1939 and repeated this in 1961 and 1972. Official studies were carried out in 1965 and 1976. It is now accepted policy that the road system should not be "improved" and the occasional congestion accepted as a temporary irritant for the summer visitor. Problems have arisen, however, on the main through routes – from Kendal to Keswick (A591), M6 to Barrow (A590) and M6 to Cockermouth and Whitehaven (A594, now A66).

380

381 A two lane dual carriageway, 48ft wide, was proposed as a bypass to
     Ambleside as early as 1964; it would have crossed these meadows
     The Fairfield horseshoe is in the distance
     Photograph Geoffrey Berry

It was hoped the construction of the M6 would stop heavy lorries
using the Kendal Keswick road but the volume has continued to rise,
encouraged by the Kendal bypass.

   Extensive "improvements" took place in the 1930's and 1950's (see
no. 369) and this in turn led to pressure by the County Council for
removal of intervening bottlenecks such as at Windermere and Grasmere
and the building of a bypass for Ambleside across the Rothay meadows.
Fortunately the Minister rejected the proposals after an inquiry in 1974.
The ban on heavy lorries introduced in 1981 should reduce the pressure
for change. The Board and the Commission will continue to resist any
proposals to expand this road.

381

382 Looking north west from Arnside Knott to the Lake District Fells
     A proposed road bridge, alongside the railway viaduct was rejected
     after a public inquiry
     Photograph Geoffrey Berry

The A596 from the M6 to Barrow poses very difficult problems,
winding over low ridges and skirting beautiful marshy estuaries. In 1970
it was proposed to link the A6 and the A596 at Lindale by a massive
viaduct across the Kent Estuary alongside the old railway line. At a
public inquiry in 1971 the Countryside Commission and other objectors
successfully opposed the proposal. While some improvements to this
road to Barrow are necessary, some of those recently completed are
excessive in scale and impact.

383

383 The new A66 bridging the River Greta north of Keswick
     Windy Brow, the Wordsworths' home in 1794 is among the trees;
     the path which Wordsworth praised leads up to Latrigg and is now
     carried across the carriageway by a concrete footbridge
     Photograph Geoffrey Berry

The A594 is now only a memory. It was the old road linking Penrith,
Keswick and Cockermouth. It was the Cumberland County Council
which proposed that it should be renumbered A66 and upgraded to a
trunk road to take traffic from the new M6 to West Cumberland. The
newly formed Department of the Environment, which now
incorporated the old Ministry of Transport, gave the route trunk road
status in 1968 and thus became responsible financially for all works on it.
Twenty three miles of the proposed new road lay within the Park. The
impact was appalling in its magnitude – dual carriageway for much of its
length, built on embankments extended 90ft out into Bassenthwaite Lake
and cutting Keswick off from its northern frame of mountains. The
proposal was wrong in scale and principle. It was also unnecessary
because an alternative route round the north of Skiddaw, outside the
Park, was available.

384 This massive embankment, 90ft wide, was built out into
     Bassenthwaite to provide space for the new road
     It is worrying to find that pollutants are being leaked into the lake
     from the material used to construct the embankment
     Photograph Geoffrey Berry

The A66 proposals were resisted by the Countryside Commission,
Board and Friends of the Lake District. The inquiry took place in 1972.
On the one hand industrial firms in West Cumbria, including British
Leyland, which proposed to establish a factory there, argued for the
quickest possible link to the M6. It was also argued that tourism would
benefit. On the other hand objectors said the road would destroy the
quality of large areas of very fine landscape, was incompatible with
national park status, was inimical to genuine tourism, and was also
unnecessary in that the alternative northern route would take only 6
minutes longer and would actually cost less. Sadly, under heavy political
pressure the road was permitted. Faith in the willingness of Government
to uphold the principles of national parks in the face even of dubious
argument, was shaken.

FORESTRY   385 Oak Wood in Borrowdale
            o   Photograph Geoffrey Berry
Broadleaved woodlands are notable for their variety of colour, shape, age
and species. They also house all manner of flowers, grasses and insects;
for instance an oak can provide a habitat for about 200 species of insects,
a conifer for about five.

386 Charcoal burners at Satterthwaite:
    a) Hut with the 'burn' incomplete
    b) The finished 'burn'
    Photographs anonymous c. 1880
    Ruskin Museum Coniston
The woodlands Wordsworth knew were almost exclusively broadleaved
– primarily oak, with birch, hazel, alder, elm and ash. Often these were
coppiced to feed charcoal and gunpowder works, and bobbin mills, and
to make hurdles. From about 1800 beech, lime and larch were
introduced; the sycamore rather earlier. If Wordsworth disliked the larch
he would have been horrified by the permanently green, regimented
spruce and pine, first introduced on a large scale by Manchester
Corporation at Thirlmere in 1908. Now, of the 60,000 acres or so of
woods in the Lake District, roughly 60% is coniferous. This widespread,
dramatic and unfortunate change in the landscape is therefore very
recent.

387 View from Great Mell Fell over Threlkeld Common towards
    Saddleback showing commercial conifer plantations. These lack
    variety, for they consist of one species of uniform age barren
    of wildlife
    Photograph Geoffrey Berry
In the absence of planning control the Lake District has been protected
from the widespread planting of conifers primarily by the 1936 agreement
(see no. 373). This continues in force and is honoured by the Forestry
Commission though there has been some difference of view in the special
area to the south west which covers Dunnerdale. In addition the Forestry
Commission has a voluntary agreement with the Planning Board and the
Countryside Commission to consult them on applications for planting
grant and on its own planting. Disputes are referred to a Regional
Advisory Committee appointed by the Forestry Commission; if that
committee cannot resolve the matter it is determined jointly by the
Minister for Agriculture and the Secretary of State for the Environment.
Both the Board and the Countryside Commission are anxious to see the
afforestation of bare land brought under proper control.

388 A wood in Kentmere grazed by sheep
    Photograph Geoffrey Berry
Planning control would not solve all the problems. Over 2700 acres of
broadleaved trees have been lost to conifers in the last 30 years. Often
this is simply the result of dense underplanting; the rapidly growing
conifers soon strangle the old trees. Sometimes the old woods are clear
felled and replanted with conifers. Another problem arises from the lack

388

of fencing of old woods. These natural stands of oak, ash and birch are often on valley sides where grazing by sheep destroys new growth and prevents natural regeneration. Sometimes, as in this photograph, the sheep debark the trees in winter. Stone walls and fencing are expensive and the loss of grazing is unwelcome to farmers. Many of these fine old woodlands are unmanaged. The Board encourages management and gives grants for fencing and replanting but its available finance is far short of the need.

389 Looking south across Thirlmere showing the incompatible
  o plantations on the lower slopes of Helvellyn
     Photograph Geoffrey Berry
Early planting of conifers was crude and expedient. Those early plantings are now soon to be harvested. This presents a chance to improve the shape of the forest and to replant with more attractive species. In the long term, given a willingness by the Water Authority to forego some income from timber, there is no reason why Thirlmere should not rival Borrowdale in the beauty and natural appearance of its woods. Clearly much also needs to be done at Ennerdale (see no.371) and in places such as Haweswater (see no.368).

390 The fine limestone pavement on Hampsfield Fell near Grange
     over Sands
     Photograph Geoffrey Berry
Banks of limestone cross the Lake District, and on the fringes especially contribute important variations to the scenery and flora.
Lime stone pavements are now protected under the Wildlife and Countryside Act 1981. The Countryside Commission and National Conservation Commission have a duty to notify the planning authority of those pavements which should be protected. The local authority then makes a formal order, binding on the landowner. The first such order was made by the Board in 1982 for the five pavements at Hampsfield Fell near Grange over Sands.

391 Approaching the Lake District 1984
    Photograph Geoffrey Berry

In the last 30 years there has been an explosion in the numbers visiting the countryside for both quiet recreation and active sports. There are no accurate figures for those visiting the National Parks but the following figures relating to organisations with a primary interest in the landscape, give an indication of the rate of growth.

No. of members in thousands

	1950	1978
Royal Society for the Protection of Birds	7	251
Youth Hostel Association	210	277
Ramblers' Association	9	29
National Trust	23	775
	1951	1976
Caravan Club	11	237
Camping Club	14	175

Roughly half the people of Britain now live within three hours' driving time of the National Park. This ready accessibility to such large numbers would have delighted those who campaigned for National Parks as places to refresh the body and uplift the spirit. It is one of the main functions of the National Park Authority to enable visitors to the Park to savour its delights. This is achieved by a policy of land acquisition either by the National Park or the National Trust; by active conservation to restore the landscape eroded by the sheer numbers of people, and by management to ensure that some areas are left fresh and quiet.

392

392 Holiday traffic impasse in Little Langdale
    Photograph Geoffrey Berry c. 1973

The Planning Board does not accept that provision should be made for every visitor to park his car wherever he wishes to go at the height of the season. That would effectively destroy the landscape that the visitor has come to see. Instead, with Commission backing, the Board makes reasonable provision (there are about 8000 car parking places in the Park) leaving the extreme congestion of July and August to act as its own deterrent. The Board also aims to preserve quiet areas of the Park (the Western Dales and the Northern and Eastern Fells), so that those who want peace and solitude can find it, even at the height of the season.

393 A launching point on Windermere
    Photograph Geoffrey Berry
One example of increasing pressure has been the growing use of powered boats on the lakes. On twenty of the smaller ones powered boats are now forbidden. On Ullswater, Coniston and Derwentwater, the introduction of a 10 mph speed limit has effectively stopped water skiing which have given gave rise to many complaints on grounds of noise and the safety of other craft, and was clearly incompatible with the concept of a national park as a place of tranquility and unmotorised physical enjoyment.

394 The eroded footpath up Helm Crag Grasmere 1982
  O Photograph Robert Thrift
Another problem not so easy to solve comes from the pressure of boots on fell paths. On some of the main routes on steep fell sides the winter weather tears away the loose material uncovered by summer walkers. The Commission, The National Park Board and the National Trust are collaborating in a project to restore some of these paths. It is time consuming, back breaking work. The project is being carefully costed so that everyone – public and Government – will be able to assess the need for finance to maintain and restore this vital feature of the national park.

395 Pitching a footpath in stone stops erosion
    Photograph Robert Thrift
The path up Helm Crag in Grassmere was restored in 1984 at a cost of £12,000. Footpath restoration is one part of the process of maintaining the Lake District landscape. In 1969 the Commission and the Board collaborated in an experiment in Upland Management – providing small sums of money to enable a specially appointed skilled man to work with local farmers in restoring stiles, bridges, walls and low level footpaths eroded by visitor pressure. The project has been so successful – and the need so great – that it now employs 27 men at an annual cost of £250,000.

396 Accommodation, teas, snacks are offered at many Lake District
    farmhouses such as this one in Kentmere
    Photograph Geoffrey Berry c. 1968
The impact of visitors has its positive side too. Footpath restoration for example creates jobs. In the Park, there are nearly 100 centres offering accommodation for outdoor activities, 22 youth hostels and over 1100 establishments offering serviced accommodation of all kinds. There are nearly 2000 holiday homes, 7000 caravan pitches and 2500 licensed tent pitches. Tourism in the National Park provides roughly 8000 jobs and generates £80,000,000 of revenue each year. By comparison agriculture employs 2800 and its annual product is worth about £31,000,000.

397 Map of Country Parks 1984
    The Countryside Commission
Country Parks are part of a national strategy to cater for visitors who
want a day in the country. Thus they supplement and protect the Lake
District and other National Parks
The tourist is now the dominating influence on the economy of the Lake
District. As upland farming faces an uncertain future it is important to
harvest tourism in ways which protect the essential qualities of the
landscape. The Planning Board maintains ten information centres where
there are expert staff whose primary job is not only to inform but to
educate the visitors so that they respect and appreciate the environment.
In England and Wales the Countryside Commission has funded 188
country parks, close to the major cities, so that day visitors can enjoy the
countryside without having to drive for hours to one of the major
national parks.

398 Dove Cottage, Shop and Museum seen from the Library 1981
  ○ Photograph David Lyons
The battles of the last 100 years seem to be diminishing in frequency
though not in scale as the National Park Board and the Countryside
Commission express their determination to protect and enhance the Lake
District landscape. The threats, such as crude afforestation and road
building, continue, and other, unforeseen issues arise to confound
optimism, but the constitutional framework is at least in place for
national debate and sensible action.
    It is to spread appreciation of the issues that the Commission has given
financial help to other organizations that encourage public understanding
of the landscape heritage. In the Lake District, the whole history of
response to its qualities has emphasised the fact that the landscape is a
living, peopled entity, accumulative of human and cultural associations,
and the richer year by year for man's involvement in it. Again, as far as

the Lake District is concerned, the feeling that it is a part of our common stock is almost inborn, and the visitor to Grasmere who knows nothing of the valley's history as a cradle of romanticism, would be exceptional. Yet the clearer perception of that aspect, and the consequent ability to participate more readily in the associations of the place, are matters of education and information. That is why it is essential that the story should be told, on the spot, and at the point of maximum potential interest and benefit.

To that end, the Countryside Commission helped in 1981 to found the new Wordsworth and Grasmere Museum, set up on the initiative of the Trustees of Dove Cottage and the Wordsworth Library, to provide the vital spark of information to the thousands of annual visitors to the Lake District. In pursuit of a wider audience still, and in a year devoted to the celebration of the National Heritage, the Commission has supported the present exhibition.

LIST OF LENDERS

Aberdeen Art Gallery and Museum
Sidney Cross Esq. Ambleside
Mrs Josephine Banner
Williamson Art Gallery Birkenhead
Birmingham Museum and Art Gallery
Towneley Hall Art Gallery Burnley
Fitzwilliam Museum Cambridge
King's College Cambridge
Trinity College Cambridge
Peter Bicknell Esq. Cambridge
Carlisle Museum and Art Gallery
The Brantwood Educational Trust Coniston
The Ruskin Museum Coniston
Mrs Susan Curwen
Derby Museum and Art Gallery
Dove Cottage Trust Grasmere
Jon Groom Esq.
Abbot Hall Art Gallery Kendal
Fitz Park Museum and Art Gallery Keswick
Ferens Art Gallery Kingston-Upon-Hull
Temple Newsam Home Leeds
Leicester Museum and Art Gallery
Usher Gallery Lincoln
Walker Art Gallery Liverpool
Liverpool University
The Alpine Club London
The British Museum London
Office of Arts and Libraries London
National Portrait Gallery London
Spink and Son London
Tate Gallery London
Christopher Wood Gallery London
G D Lockett Esq.
Manchester City Art Gallery
Whitworth Art Gallery Manchester
David Nash Esq.
Laing Art Gallery Newcastle
Ashmolean Museum Oxford
Reading Museum and Art Gallery
The Viscount Rochdale
J Wordsworth Esq.
St. Anne's School Windermere

THE ASSOCIATES OF THE VICTORIA AND ALBERT MUSEUM

The following companies and individuals take a particular interest in the Museum and channel their support through the Museum's charity, The Associates of the V&A:

ASSOCIATES
Arthur Andersen & Company
The Baring Foundation
Bonas and Company
Christie's
Commercial Union Assurance Company
Colnaghi & Company
Charles Letts (Holdings) Limited
Mobil
Oppenheimer Charitable Trust
Rose and Hubble Limited
J Sainsbury plc
Sotheby's
John Swire and Sons Limited
Thames Television

INDIVIDUAL BENEFACTORS AND ASSOCIATES
The Sirdar and Begum Aly Aziz
Sir Duncan Oppenheim
Mrs Basil Samuel

SPONSORS
Through The Associates of the V&A, the following companies, organisations, and individuals have sponsored Galleries, Exhibitions, Scholarships, Lectures, Concerts and Catalogues at the V&A since 1981:
The Acquarius Trust
Cariplo Bank
The Countess Ahlefeldt
B.A.D.A.
Bankers Trust Company
The Baring Foundation
The Countryside Commission
G P and J Baker Limited
The Daily Telegraph
Express Newspapers plc
H J Heinz Charitable Trust
Ilford Limited
Jaegar
Sirge Lifar
The Linbury Trust
The Merrill Trust
Mobil
Pearson plc
Pirelli
Mrs Basil Samuel
Trusthouse Forte
United Technologies

THE FRIENDS OF THE VICTORIA AND ALBERT MUSEUM

Existing within the framework of The Associates, the following Corporate Friends give their support to the Museum:

CORPORATE FRIENDS
Alan Hutchison Publishing Company Limited
Albert Amor Limited
Antiques Porcelain Company
Artist Cards Limited
Ashstead Decorative and Fine Arts Society
Asprey and Company
Bank of England Arts Society
Bankers Trust Company
Blairman and Sons Limited
British Petroleum
Chase Manhattan Bank
Cobra and Bellamy
Coutts and Company Bankers
Crabtree and Evelyn Limited
Cyril Humphris
Donohoe
Goldsmiths Company
Hotspur Limited
John Keil Limited
Kennedy Brookes plc
Ian Logan Limited
London and Provincial Antique Dealers' Association
Madame Tussaud's Limited
Marks and Spencer plc
The Medici Society Limited
Mendip Decorative and Fine Arts Society
Barbara Minto Limited
W H Patterson Fine Arts Limited
Pearson plc
Charles Pfister Incorporated
Phillips Auctioneers
S J Phillips plc
Phillips Petroleum
Pickering and Chatto
RTZ Services Limited
South Molton Antiques Limited
Spink and Son Limited
Stair and Company
The Fine Art Society Limited
The Wellcome Foundation
William Bedford Antiques
Winifred Williams
World of Islam Festival Trust

INDIVIDUAL FRIENDS
Support the Museum both financially and by giving voluntary help, thus forming a personal link with the V&A.